MW00582803

THE ZEN OF PUZZLES

The Zen of
PUZZLES

A Ritual for Accessing
the Subconcious Mind

ANITAH L. GOMBOS

LUMINARE PRESS

WWW.LUMINAREPRESS.COM

This is a work of fiction and the characters are not based on
any person, living or deceased.

The Zen of Puzzles
© 2018 Anitah L. Gombos

All rights reserved. This book or any portion thereof may not be
reproduced or used in any manner whatsoever without the express written
permission of the publisher, except for the use of brief quotations in a
book review.

Printed in the United States of America

Cover Design: Claire Flint Last

Luminare Press
438 Charnelton St., Suite 101
Eugene, OR 97401
www.luminarepress.com

LCCN: 2018937258
ISBN: 978-1-944733-64-3

With great gratitude, this book is dedicated to my family, friends, and contrarians, both seen and unseen, whose love, support, and challenges have brought me to this miraculous moment.

You know who you are.

Prologue

I n the depths of winter, it was easy to reach for the warmer times of the heart when laughter and love flowed generously. Steely gray clouds sucked light from the sky as they advanced, foretelling the coming snow, leaving behind only January gloom. A typical New York winter's day. Though I tried to chase away shadows by turning on every light in the house, grief still stalked me. To achieve peace with this relentless pursuer, I know I must first surrender my own inner darkness. But how?

She had been dead five months and I couldn't seem to get over it. She would certainly not be happy I continued to mainline numbing sadness. I could almost see her standing in front of me. "Darling Rachel, I died. I didn't leave you. You really need to pull yourself together."

She would have paired her remarks with a gesture I recognized was code for "Get on with it." Just the thought made me laugh and unlocked my spirit a little. Yes, it was way past time. I threw up my mental hands and said to this unseen specter, "Okay, Aunt Grace. You win. I need to do something and I promise I'll do it now."

It was a rare Saturday when my daughter and her snickerdoodle puppy were spending the weekend with my parents, and my husband was enjoying a bit of male bonding over racquetball. For the first time in a long time, the cat and I had the house to ourselves. However, I was so accustomed to the distractions of constant commotion and child-chatter, the quiet felt almost unsettling. When the heck had that happened? When did silence become a stranger and not the comfortable companion I had known forever? Why did my taken-for-granted *usual* now feel so very *alien*? (The cat, however, was hugely happy.)

Perhaps it was time to go through the "Aunt Grace Box" I hadn't touched since she died—the one carefully hidden behind the pile of sweaters at the back of my closet. Maybe when I finally opened the box, it would release a cloud of fairy dust and magically lift my malaise. Sure. And then maybe I could become the next queen of England.

Those who loved me were concerned about how distant I was, a half-here version of myself. They couldn't seem to reach me. However, I recently figured out what was going on. Deep down, I believed if I stopped mourning her, I would lose her.

Somehow, I had become a woeful actor performing in a mindless melodrama not suitable for even a two-show run. Enough! I was finally ready to walk off the stage and shut down the production. Yes, it was way past time.

I knew what to do. I had gone through ripping grief before. She taught me how to win internal battles when they tried hard to lay me low.

I took the box downstairs to the living room and started a fire. While it was growing to a proper blaze, I brewed a pot of fresh coffee; walked back to the way-more-cheerful living room; and placed the "I love you, Mommy" mug on a side table. Curling up in the corner of the couch, I framed my intention and spoke it aloud. "I call upon my heart's inner knowing to help me see what needs to be seen and understand what needs to be understood. I do this with the intention of letting go the constricting emotions which bind me so I can fully return to happiness and grace and be more loving and present to myself and those in my life. With great gratitude, I thank the Divine within for supporting me in this process."

I had asked for help. Now all I needed to do was open myself to receive it.

One of the most significant times Aunt Grace and I had shared filled a four-day period about five years before she died, a life-changing pause. She used the practice of working a jigsaw puzzle as a metaphor for engaging life and through the process, helped me get to the other side of a very tough transition. Within the puzzle space, she essentially handed me her life's legacy of wisdom and courage at a time I most needed it.

The box held the touchstones of this inheritance and perhaps—just perhaps—I could wrap myself in her mantle and gradually grow into its immensity. While the petulant part of me resolutely held her at arm's length, the adult part, still alive and well (though getting a bit bored with my continued moodiness), trusted that even now, she would always be there for me. Okay, I'd give it a go.

Resolution made, it felt natural to also ask for *her* help in making this putting-on-the-mantle moment real. "Bring it on, Aunt Grace." Immediately, I smelled a hint of her perfume and I almost—almost—freaked out. She once again had made her presence clearly known. Where had she been all this time? Or more accurately, where had *I* been?

Written during the "dark time," I read through the journals with my thoughts about applying her life-as-a-puzzle insights to my life. Then I listened to her recordings describing each phase of the puzzle process. I was surprised. I had forgotten how amazing her thoughts were, and I sucked them up like a desert survivor gulping water. Her perceptive, down-to-earth suggestions for handling the human and spiritual aspects of life, laced with big doses of compassion and humor, touched me in unexpected ways.

Aunt Grace named her approach to puzzling, *The Zen of Puzzles,* the ability to be fully present and listen closely to what is needed in order to respond with integrity. Doing this in right timing offers *aha moments* of awakening and understanding (if we choose to accept them), delivered not through the mind's logic but through the heart's knowing. She said living life this way takes practice but the effort is well worth it. I found this to be true for me and when I regularly practiced, life flowed more easily. Why, then, had I stopped paying attention? Was I using her death as an excuse to not live as my truest self? Hmm.

I always meant to assemble her ideas into a book and perhaps this was the time to get serious. She had given me permission to publish her thoughts if I believed they would be helpful to others. Yup. I was definitely a believer! Time to get on with it.

Richard, my husband, called to remind me he would not be home for dinner and, as I was deep into Aunt Grace's puzzle wisdom, this worked just fine for me. I guess he heard something in my voice, though, because he asked what I was up to. When I told him, he was pleased but a little wary, not knowing what feelings it would stir up and what version of myself he would find when he returned.

Voice quivering a little, I assured him this was the beginning of turning the corner on my grief, and I apologized for being distant the last few months. He could tell I was beginning to cry. Always leading with kindness, Richard said he understood and I should take as much time as I needed to do what was right for me. After a final "I love you," we said our goodbyes. (Within an hour, flowers arrived with a reminder, "All is well," a favorite Aunt Grace phrase. I am very grateful for this man.)

After that Saturday, time passed as it always did but with a healthy twist. I spent several months mentally organizing the puzzle material and wrapping words around what I wanted to say. In the end, a workable book outline materialized. Then for the next year, I wrote in dribs and drabs as I found the time to move thoughts from head to laptop. This cathartic process produced a compendium of the events of my special Aunt-Grace time, a step-by-step, how-to guide about gathering valuable life clues by working jigsaw puzzles.

During this process, as I immersed myself in the ideas she had introduced and remembrances of what I later experienced as a result, my inner grayness began to lift like the fog in sunlight, and a warming rightness took its place. My heart began to unfreeze and I could finally breathe. I could touch the people I loved. Once more, I was back in my center

We all need an Aunt Grace in our lives and if you did not have the good fortune to be blessed with a wise, compassionate, funny woman who was always there for you, then I gladly share her legacy. I do this with great anticipation, trusting you will fall in love with her as I did and perhaps have your own *aha moments* along the way. If you keep your heart open to what she has to say, your life can surely change.

Her remarkable story illustrates how one woman's life, lived fully and richly, can influence and inspire many others. May this "beacon on a hill," a symbol accurately representing Aunt Grace's luminous life, motivate you to shine your own light more brightly. Let it be so.

Chapter One

Meet Aunt Grace

I watched out the front bay window broadly framing the almost-black Atlantic Ocean as my father went to greet her and carry her suitcases. His golden retriever, Gus, helped by racing around and barking from behind as if herding them to the front door.

She still stood regally tall, and not even her days-from-now ninetieth birthday could slow her down, diminish her strength, or dim the sassy gleam in her eyes. I felt the familiar thrill always arriving when I saw her, knowing an adventure would inevitably unfold.

My father laughed as he bent his head from his 6'3" frame to hear more easily what she was saying from her own 5'8" elevation. They were quite a sight—her sleekly silver hair hinting at what his salted black hair might look like when it grew up. Though she charmed everyone, few loved and liked her the way we did—my father, mother, brother, and I. Few could relate to her story. Many did not bother to try.

The State of Grace

Great Aunt Grace was not my aunt "by blood," though she lived with my Great Uncle George for twenty-five years before he died four years ago. I had known her for the greater part of my thirty-three years and we all embraced her as "Aunt Grace," though the rest of my father's starchy family refused to acknowledge her at all. I still could not fathom why they thought she was a gold digger. Grace came to the relationship with Uncle George as a wealthy woman and inherited nothing from him except the house they shared.

Uncle George's three children could not really complain as they were most tidily taken care of in his will. However, the two oldest persisted in righteously ranting about Grace to any hijacked listener. I was happy these two nasties would not be coming to Aunt Grace's birthday party. However, Julia, the youngest, would arrive for the weekend—Julia, the sole exception to their strange shared gene pool.

Why all the raised eyebrows and snide whispers? Well, Aunt Grace had "a past." An only child, she was raised in a small town in Indiana during the mid-1920s. Her father served as a minister in a miniscule farming community where everyone knew everything about everybody and clung to opinions passed from generation to generation. Grace enjoyed a happy, normal childhood until her mother died when she was eleven—the crucial, almost-teenager time.

Without her mother's balancing presence, her father

became angry and embittered—enraged at the fickle God he had faithfully served for a great many years, the God who dealt him such a crippling blow. Up to this point, Grace's father paid more attention to his congregation than to her. But conditions changed after her mother's death when Grace became central to her father's ministry, a role she detested. Almost overnight, she was forced to take on the church work her mother, as the minister's wife, had supported.

In her newly defined adult role, Grace was her father's representative at all the church's "female functions." Dutifully, she oversaw bake sales; worked alongside members of the cleaning committee; participated in the quilting circle; sold tickets for the building raffles; and attended the many weekly and seasonal "women's work" activities.

Grace felt trapped. She was given little time to herself and certainly no time to be with her school friends, but she hid her growing resentment well, trusting she would eventually escape. Until then, she was careful to do everything the best she could. To survive, she found ways to keep her father from directing his increasingly volatile anger at his daughter instead of his God. Frankly, Grace was afraid of her father's blind rages, and it was only a matter of time before he finally snapped and completely lost control.

When Grace reached puberty the following year, the gangly, awkward girl quickly transformed into a crowd-stopping beauty. Her father became even more strict, more demanding, and suddenly, more suspicious. His innate harshness roared to the forefront, and more and more, he carried on like an Old Testament prophet shouting about God's disgust for harlots, corrupters of upright men. New Testament forgiveness and compassion were never part of his narrative.

From the pulpit, her father stridently delivered apocryphal warnings of retribution to both the church community and to her. He exhorted them to faithfully tread salvation's straight-and-narrow road, while painstakingly detailing the hellacious consequences of their evil-doing. Everyone squirmed during his fist-pounding sermons, but no church member was more severely admonished than Grace to "always do God's will" and conduct herself as a "proper Christian woman." She was fourteen.

Grace was forbidden to date, dance, or sing. When her father caught her listening to the jazz music he and her mother had danced to, he smashed the radio against a wall. She also could not wear age-appropriate clothes. Grace was embarrassed by her frumpy shapeless dresses and grandma shoes from the mission box when all the girls wore fashionable cinched-waist, mid-calf dresses and cute strappy shoes.

As much as he tried, though, her father could not hide Grace's innate beauty. Despite the oversized clothing, boys still chased after her, much to his alarm and fury.

Whenever her father saw her talking to a boy, he would yank her inside the house and accuse her of seducing the boys and leading them astray. He compared her so often to Eve, the original fallen woman, Grace felt she should just eat the damned apple and be done with it.

Her father reproached her for engaging in lewd acts, of drinking and smoking, of general mayhem and debauchery. During these rants, Grace remained silent, though mentally arguing she could not have possibly managed to do any of those things, no matter how intriguing they might sound. While storming at her and stomping around the room, Grace, with saving humor, imagined her father as a mad little bug, spastically jumping up and down in an empty pickle jar while she tightly screwed on the lid to finally shut him up. Her images usually deflected the pain of these tormented diatribes. Usually—but not always. The fear always remained.

The Great Escape

By the time she was sixteen, Grace had endured her father long enough. She was done with her little life and steadfastly resolved to leave it behind. She secretly wrote to one of her mother's cousins in New York—the one who could never figure out why her mother had married her father in the first place—and when she explained her situation, she found a sympathetic ear. She also found a place to stay. Feeling freer than she had since her mother died, Grace took enough money from church donations to get to New York, buy new clothes, and find a job.

She departed on a Saturday when her father was occupied by an all-day planning meeting with the church council, followed directly by the Saturday-night service.

Grace left a note telling him where she had gone; gave him an I.O.U. for the loan; and walked out the door with only one change of clothes, her underwear, and a photo of her mother. She would buy new clothes in New York.

Grace took a dilapidated bus to Philadelphia where she splurged and boarded a more modern train, not wanting to arrive in New York on a shabby bus. Though the ride was uneventful, Grace was thrilled to watch the countryside pass by, bringing her ever closer to the city which had been in her dreams for months. The excitement kept building the closer she got to this promised land, and she fantasized herself a heroine—the main character in an adventure novel—ready to take an enormous bite of the Big Apple.

By the time a taxi dropped Grace off at her new home, however, her father had already called to disown this "ungrateful slut" and commanded she never return to either his home or the town she thanklessly abandoned. (Her father was always fond of commandments.) This twist was never part of her imaginary plot, though Grace ruefully realized she should have expected it. Surprisingly, she felt a dull pain—perhaps a touch of sadness. Her mother was buried there. But being pragmatic, Grace quickly added her father's dismissal to the stack of reasons why she had been smart to put the town and her father behind her.

In pre-World War II days when women were expected to fill traditional housekeeping and child-raising roles, few job opportunities outside the home were available to them. But Grace needed and wanted to work, not caring what kind of job she landed as long as it did not involve sitting behind a desk all day. Repeating the tedious sameness filling her recent life would have driven her crazy, so she wanted a job working with customers.

To look the part of a competent professional, Grace shopped for the kind of clothes she would actually enjoy wearing. At last, she was able to buy flowy print dresses with cinched waists; A-line skirts rising daringly to the knee; high-waist blouses with wide padded shoulders that created a more pronounced nipped-in silhouette; and low heels (with straps!) with a belt and purse to match. Determined to find a coat with a fur collar—in her mind, the height of luxury and style—she found a simple design, making her feel oh-so-good. Of course, she simply could not forget an elegant hat and everyday gloves.

With a newly found sense of style and an abundance of untrammeled optimism, Grace carefully purchased second-hand clothes in several upscale areas. Once she accessorized them with beautiful scarves and tasteful jewelry, she felt and looked like a million bucks.

Grace ended up selling perfume in a high-end department store where after only ten months, a man who owned a top modeling agency discovered her and literally changed her life. Feeling once again like a fictional heroine—this time in a modern fairy tale—Grace became a well-paid model, an instant member of a glittering world she never knew existed. She was soon able to pay back her father and offer her mother's cousin and husband additional monthly rent for their third-floor room.

Becoming a model was a true turning point for Grace. Earning a comfortable amount of money gave her more options but unfortunately, the once supportive atmosphere in the house turned decidedly chilly the longer she modeled. The couple who had welcomed her as family now became distant and disapproving. They strongly condemned her new work, believing models were essentially prostitutes in nice clothes—or at least this was what they often said when she was not in the room (but loudly enough for her to hear). They also lamented how heartbroken her "sainted mother" would be if she were still alive and "saw what Grace was up to."

Though Grace understood they were probably worried about her (and also about what their friends and neighbors might think), she soon realized for their sake and her sanity, she needed to find another place to live. Within weeks of making up her mind, Grace found a lovely low-rent apartment to share with a friend from her perfume-selling days—a rental record even in those days. Everyone was greatly relieved.

Her time in New York swept by in a whirlwind of shoots, makeup, wardrobe changes, and endless scheduling. However, after two and a half years of modeling, Grace began to find the work draining and monotonous, finally admitting to herself she couldn't stand it. Though her iconic blonde-hair-and-blue-eyes willowy beauty earned her a premium wage, she could not envision spending her youth sitting still in front of a camera for hours on end. For Grace, the work became dull and uncomfortable—almost as dull and uncomfortable as doing church work, and for her, this was quite a statement.

Socially, she had quickly figured out many of the men who sniffed around models in those days were generally insufferable, and they expected either their money or their charm to get them what they wanted. Grace saw them as dimwitted annoyances and chose to spend time in her apartment reading rather than be doggy-bagged home as dessert after dinner.

During the week, Grace led a very solitary life. On weekends, however, she roamed New York, almost living in museums and taking in as many concerts, ballets, and Broadway shows she could. Occasionally, Grace was escorted by men she met and found interesting, though she never developed a long-term relationship with any of them. She lived a pleasant but predictable life. Okay for the short term, but definitely not enough for Aunt Grace.

What Happens in Vegas

One day, during a lunch conversation, another agency model, Dorothea, told Grace she was giving up modeling for something more exciting. Like a heat-seeking missile, Aunt Grace mentally zeroed in on a potential new life.

Dorothea explained she was trading New York winters for Las Vegas heat and already had asked Vegas connections to get her a job as a showgirl. The Fabulous Flamingo Hotel and Casino had just opened and they were looking for showgirls to perform between acts. Then and there, Grace decided to go with her. She could always learn to dance and, given the hours of practice she'd had at church, she was already a good singer. She was more than ready to cut loose and really enjoy herself as any normal twenty-one-year-old woman would. She gladly gave up her dull days and quiet nights.

Leaving New York and landing a showgirl job was relatively easy, and Grace was thrilled to find she loved dancing and singing and was actually talented at both. She loved the entire casino scene—the costumes, music, lights, sounds, laughter, and, most of all, the chance to be on stage.

She and Dorothea both worked at the Flamingo and shared a small, two-bedroom apartment, falling into an uncomplicated routine of work, parties, and sleep. After just a month, Grace woke up one morning realizing, at long last, she was finally having fun. Life felt much freer and easier in Las Vegas.

This comfortable routine lasted for about fourteen months, until Grace was unexpectedly offered a different job in the Flamingo's top-billed show. She would be part of a select group of showgirls who backed Jimmy Durante, the headline act. It was a high-profile spot and came with a lot more money. Grace was thrilled.

Dorothea, however, did not take the news well and began accusing Grace of sleeping her way to a better job even though she knew this was untrue. Her lies infected the last few weeks on her old job, and at home, the jealous nastiness escalated. Consequently, Dorothea's bitterness galvanized Grace into finding her own apartment. She was certainly not going to allow Dorothea or anyone else to step on her dreams or keep her from having fun.

For the first time, Grace was totally on her own and savored the sweetness of not answering to anyone but herself. Deep down, Grace knew she was on her way to enormous success and nothing was going to slow her down.

Being strikingly beautiful in a high-profile show in a high-roller casino in a high-stakes town was Grace's ticket to a glamorous, over-the-top lifestyle she had only read about. She was swept up in new experiences and sensations and lustily dove into her new life as if into a vat of champagne she couldn't lap up fast enough. She dated, she drank, she seduced, she drank, she accepted lavish gifts, she drank, she went on expensive holidays, she drank.

Grace did everything to excess until months later, she finally paused. She looked—really looked—in the mirror and saw a somewhat hardened version of herself emptily staring back. Overwhelmed, she accepted the hideous truth. She had become unmoored and was quickly disappearing into darkness. She had mutated into someone she didn't recognize and was now the main character in the smuttiest kind of cheap pulp fiction imaginable. Was this her new life? Maybe she would think about it later.

Only a few weeks after this disturbing insight, awareness again sucker-punched Grace when she woke one morning with a raging thirst. She was in an enormous, richly appointed hotel room, but she was clueless about where she was and why she was there. All she could remember was partying with a few men on Friday night after work. She remembered nothing else, and this really scared her.

A much older man sauntered in with a smirk on his face and offered her orange juice. Grace knew enough not to drink it, realizing it was probably drugged. When she asked what day it was, she was horrified to learn two days had passed. What in the world had gone on here? What in God's name had they done to her? God. Her father would have felt gleefully vindicated.

She was sore all over and when she stiffly made her way to the bathroom to shower and get dressed, she was alarmed to see large purpling bruises down her thighs, on her breasts, on her buttocks, and on her neck and back. Sickened and deeply alarmed, she skipped the shower; threw on her clothes; and left the room as quickly as she could; passing two other men on her way out the door. When one lunged and attempted to stop her, she kicked him as hard as she could in an apparently overused part of his anatomy, and she ran.

Grace caught a cab in front of the casino and rode home. Once she knew she was safe in her apartment, she stumbled to the bathroom and vomited what little food remained. Then she stood for hours under a hot shower; shaking with unremembered horror; trying to feel clean again; sobbing until there were no more tears.

She became almost reclusive after the "lost weekend."

She felt damaged. She felt stupid. She stopped dating and did not accept the many invitations that continued to come her way.

Grace never saw the men again, the three who had essentially kidnapped and raped her, nor did she file a police report. She learned they were part of the mob family Bugsy Siegel had brought with him when he opened the Flamingo, so why should she even bother? They would all be on his side. Siegel was now a feared "front-page gangster" and had bought off almost all the politicians and police in Las Vegas. Those who weren't in his pocket left him alone knowing what would happen if they crossed him or his gang.

Grace was also too ashamed and knew the police would probably blame her for letting this happen. Her emotions became more and more chaotic. She barely survived a horrible night when, feeling helpless and hopeless, she thought about suicide just to end the torment.

Eventually, the party people deserted her. She had no family, no friends. She went from being happier than she had ever been in her entire life to feeling totally alone. With self-revelatory disgust, Grace admitted to herself all her father's predictions about her had come true. She had disastrously lost her way. She was a fallen woman, a seductress, a foul sinner. Perhaps her father had seen her corruption all along. Maybe he was right after all.

Redemption Comes from Within

Then a voice deep inside she never heard before roared, "No!" The familiarly unfamiliar voice insisted she would *not* become part of her father's crazy nightmare and lose who she knew herself to be. She *would* find a way back to her center. She *would* survive this and she would do it *on her own terms.* She listened. She agreed. In that pivotal moment, armed with angry courage and a restored will to live, Grace chose to not just survive, but to truly thrive. She would regain her self-respect and forge a different life.

Grace continued to work at the casino, but she asked if she could learn how to be a dealer at one of the tables instead of remaining a dancer. (She had told her boss what happened when she lost three days of work and he had been surprisingly sympathetic.) There were no women croupiers in the casino at the time and this seemed like an outrageous request, but management was smart enough to know her looks alone would be the magnet drawing a lot of men to her table. Grace learned how to run a high-stakes blackjack table which quickly became the most popular table on the floor.

When she was not working, Grace studied for her high school equivalency and easily passed the exam. After this first step, she took correspondence courses and pursued a four-year degree. She surprised herself by discovering an uncanny aptitude for finance, and her studies gave her the confidence to begin investing her savings. More than anything, Grace wanted to secure her financial future because it would mean she would never need to rely on anybody ever again. She *would* become her own woman and support herself. Furthermore, she was clear about never marrying. She had learned the hard way what men were really like.

She seemed to have the Midas touch and instinctively picked the right high-yield securities. Within four years, Grace converted her savings, her generous salary, and her even-more-generous tips into the gold of real estate and astute investments. Las Vegas was booming and real estate skyrocketed. In time, these investments brought her the wealth and security she craved. Grace knew she could now take care of herself no matter what happened.

She carefully constructed her safe world but like a trite plot from a late-night B movie, Grace caught the eye of a wealthy New York financier who traveled regularly through Las Vegas on his way to San Francisco. Once again, she became a storybook heroine—this time in a romance novel.

She was almost twenty-six and he was forty-three, divorced, no children. In an act of rebellion against his own prim-and-proper upbringing, Harold wooed her, won her, and married her, though it took him almost two years.

Initially, Grace was skittish and untrusting but over time, she began believing there could be a different kind of man, one who was unlike those who had scarred her. With trust came love and acceptance, and Grace decided to give Harold a chance. However, she was not foolish and knew this unorthodox relationship would cause trouble with his pedigreed family when they returned to New York, and it most certainly did—big time. But Grace and Harold simply chose not to care and would frequently tell each other there was nothing like a little scandal and rebellion to get the blood moving.

Grace and Harold were stereotypically *madly in love*. They lived their lives fully; traveled well and widely; threw parties frequently; and enjoyed each other's company enormously. To the bafflement of many who predicted their union would never last, they became the embodiment of what a happy relationship could look like. Over the years, Grace's questionable past receded into the background as most in their social circle came to simply accept her as Harold's lovely young wife.

Their unshakeable and colorful marriage lasted almost twenty years before Harold suddenly died in bed making energetic love to his always enthusiastic wife. As Grace mentioned years later, he had died smiling.

Grace inherited most of his considerable fortune. Many assumed she would become a merry widow, but Grace withdrew from the spotlight and lived as a recluse for almost three years. Men who wanted to date her were repeatedly turned away until finally their persistent calls stopped coming.

Grace was devastated when Harold died. Her life's firm foundation suddenly and completely crumbled. She was only forty-eight and still had a lot of life to live. The problem was, Grace was clueless about how she was going to fill all those years. She retreated into herself to figure out who she had become and to plot a new course for herself, one that sadly did not include Harold.

While walking at sunrise on a Maine beach, Grace had a vision of her next step. A well-formed plan unfolded in her mind to do the work she had always done best and satisfied her the most. She decided to devote her time to increasing Harold's wealth and bringing his legacy of compassionate kindness to the world.

When Grace focused her considerable intellect and shrewd street-smarts on Harold's investments, she was able to triple their combined assets within eight years. Along with investing, she started a foundation to fund shelters for abused women, some of the first in the country.

Abuse was a topic rarely spoken about at a time in "polite society" when women were still expected to be good wives and obey their husbands "no matter what." Abuse? It must be the woman's fault. Within her social circle, there were a few hardliners who thought her shameful for focusing attention on such private matters and would round out their gossip with, "Well considering her background, it's really not surprising." Of course, Grace ignored them and continued to do exactly as she pleased.

She knew too many victims of abuse from working in New York and Las Vegas to be slowed down by the thorny opinions of a few sheltered hothouse roses. Over time, she engaged many willing and influential society matrons in fundraising efforts for their less-fortunate sisters. They, in turn, convinced their well-connected husbands to support legislation to better protect women. Helping abused women became fashionable. She could almost hear Harold laughing.

Returning

About five years after Harold's death, Grace reentered New York's social world. Though some long-memoried critics still remained dubious about her interests and activities, none could deny Grace's magnetic attraction or minimize the impact of her good work. Fascination with what this unorthodox woman would do next ran high. Grace was frequently pictured on society pages being escorted around New York on the arm of one prominent man after another, but these affairs never seemed to last long—that is, until she met Great Uncle George.

Great Uncle George was my father's uncle, and everyone adored him for his humor, wisdom, and effervescent curiosity about life. He was married young to someone with the proper social status and was gladly divorced after enduring ten years with a shrill, greedy, unappeasable wife who managed to present him with three unhappy children. The whole sad experience convinced George he was clearly not cut out for marriage. He was linked to a succession of women but none managed to capture his heart.

His strange and estranged wife did everything she could to turn his children against him, so Uncle George saw them infrequently and under strained conditions. Therefore, he directed all his love to his nieces and nephews who vied for his time and glad attention. Uncle George, my father, and his brother were especially close, and when Dad talks about his adventures camping and fishing (and later clubbing and traveling) with his Uncle George and Dad's brother, James, his voice still catches a bit as he reminisces about good times and good men now gone.

When George first met Grace at one of her charity events, he was instantly and irrationally attracted to her, and proceeded to run as fast as he could in the opposite direction. He was certain this very appealing woman could upset his well-defined, comfortable existence. George steered clear of Grace and habitually left a room as soon as she walked in. Grace noticed and thought this was both funny and endearing. She understood exactly what was going on with Uncle George and took a few steps to move things along. Therefore, he was dismayed to find himself always seated next to her at private dinners.

Grace later admitted she plotted these seating arrangements after quickly realizing George was incapable of making the first move. When Grace met George, she too had felt an instant attraction, the first since Harold's death. On the spot, Grace decided to get to know George better. He never had a chance and, apparently, he never really wanted one.

They dated for almost eighteen months before Grace scandalously moved in with him and messed up his every favorite routine. Uncle George was reborn, and though he was persistent in his attempts to convince Grace to marry him, she always gently but firmly refused. Wise woman that she was, Grace knew marriage would alienate his distant children even more as they were already fretting about their future inheritance. She convinced George living happily "in sin" would keep their relationship alive and interesting. And it did.

We did not see much of Aunt Grace when Uncle George suddenly died from a brain aneurysm after celebrating their twenty-fifth anniversary. Once more, she went into seclusion to figure out how to live by herself again.

Though she occasionally dated, Aunt Grace never became serious about another man. She thought having two great loves in her life was enough for her and simply chose to enjoy male companionship without the commitments.

Reunion

Bringing my mind back to the present, I smiled and thought about her last ten months. Aunt Grace has been with what she describes as a "much younger man," a seventy-six-year-old, semi-retired real estate developer from Italy who satisfies her and makes her laugh. He has a flat in New York not far from Aunt Grace's home, and they are frequently together when he is in the country. I recalled my last conversation with her as I watched Grace approach. Her coat flapped wildly as the wind bringing a predicted nor'easter swept her to the front door.

How did she do it? My one attempt at marriage ended

two months earlier after only three years. Like Grace, I did not have children, but I had grown up anticipating the Norman Rockwell life of adoring husband and happy children gathered around a Thanksgiving table with a cute puppy hovering nearby. Well, I might as well throw this dream out with the turkey scraps.

I hadn't held onto the man I thought was my *first* real love. I'd blown our relationship. Moreover, I could hear my reproductive clock ticking as loudly as a pre-digital bomb. (Another reference about explosions? What did this foreshadow?) I didn't even own my own dog, for heaven's sake, though I enjoyed sharing Gus. Well, this could get downright depressing.

"Get ahold of yourself, Rachel," I thought with just a tinge of self-disgust and a lot of mental eye rolling. "You're getting whiney again. Aunt Grace is here. Put on your happy face."

These thoughts swirled in my mind as I met them in the foyer. I looked at Aunt Grace and all I could do was smile—genuinely smile. She made me feel very, very happy. When I saw the understanding in her eyes, my own eyes filled with an ocean of unshed tears. She knew. She always knew.

I momentarily stepped into my ten-year-old self, running to her when I had been teased by boys because I was exceptionally tall compared to their hormonally challenged, not-growing-yet bodies. (Yes, I have a history of being a bit whiney when things go wrong.) They said I looked like a stupid beanpole monster from outer space or a dumb rubber band that had been stretched too much and looked creepy. (At this age, name-calling skills are still rather undeveloped.)

As she did many years ago, Grace simply hugged me, held me, and rocked me slightly until my tension began to drain. I was home and I would be all right. Later, the words would come.

My mother hurried from the kitchen to offer her own greetings, hugs, and kisses. Grace was the same height as my mother and, in more ways than one, they saw eye-to-eye. I watched the two most important women in my life as they reconnected.

My brother and his wife would not arrive until Friday, and I was almost giddy thinking about the four days I would have Aunt Grace and my parents all to myself. Let's not forget Gus who was wagging his tail and running in circles he was so excited. I felt like doing to same. Already, I was feeling much better.

Chapter Two

The Purpose of Puzzling

I followed my father as he carried Aunt Grace's two suit-cases up the stairs to the guest bedroom overlooking the back garden. Aunt Grace always said that when she slept, she preferred the steadfastness of a garden to the restlessness of the ocean. She always picked this room rather than the water-facing front guestroom at the end of the hall to the left the stairs. For Grace, oceans were for shaking things up and were there to help us think new thoughts and dream new dreams, while a garden offered peace and rest at day's end. Poetic and prophetic.

Gina and Robert would be happy to sleep in his former bedroom to the right of mine with its Jack-and-Jill bathroom connecting the two bedrooms on the other side of the hallway. When we were growing up, he hated the Jill stuff lining the counter, but he learned to suck it up. We got through these territorial disputes and remain very close. He's both my brother and my friend.

I sat on the edge of the bed while she unpacked her clothes and smiled as I watched her open the closet to hang an ice-blue nightgown with its matching silk robe, both heavy with French lace. It was exactly like the set she had given me for my last birthday except mine was forest green to complement my black hair and green eyes.

Grace believed a woman needed a wardrobe of lovely nightwear the same as she needed beautiful daytime clothes—outer expressions of who she was. Though I loved its luxurious softness against my skin, the nightgown was not fully appreciated by my former husband who was more turned on by the oversized NASCAR tee-shirt he purchased for me the same birthday.

My sophisticated investment banker husband really loved his hobbies and toys, especially racing toys—and it made him happy to see their logos on the many pieces of clothing he purchased for me at events. Looking back, I realized it was his way of bringing me into his world and perhaps branding me as his own. I felt guilty for obviously making him feel increasingly insecure about our relationship. Perhaps this was his unspoken, even unconscious attempt, to hold onto me. This realization also made me really sad.

Getting Down to It

Grace and I chatted amicably of inconsequential things and caught up with each other's lives. I talked about work and my forever-friend she knew well, Fiona, and she told me about her charity functions and Antonio, her lover. After putting everything away in either closet or bathroom, Grace sat next to me and said, "How are you really doing, Rachel? Talk to me."

We had frequently touched base when I was going through my divorce, but this was the first time I was actually with her. In her presence, I felt the tug of her authority, demanding only what was true. What should I say?

"Rachel, I can see your mind going a million miles a minute. Slow down. Breathe. Just open your heart and tell me how you're doing."

I trembled as a mega-quake ripped through me, shaking loose granite words, demolishing trust and hope in their path. Anger and blame. Shame and confusion. Recrimination and self-doubt. Feeling stuck and not knowing what to do about it. The aftershocks of fierce feelings continued to run their course.

A tsunami of tears followed the quake, churning the rubble of emotional devastation I hadn't even known was there. I sobbed for what felt like years. Aunt Grace gently held me until I stilled.

When the first wave passed, I was calmer, though a second wave quickly followed, swelling and crashing around me, sweeping me along with its force. This second wave came without tears but stirred up messy thoughts about my incomprehensible divorce.

After my graduate and post-graduate studies, state licensing process, and years of solidifying my career as a head pharmacist, I'd felt like I could finally relax, find a nice guy to marry, and raise a family. I had been so careful. I was not going to settle for an almost-good-enough partner as I believed some of my friends had done. I was going to find my perfect mate.

Jonathan and I had known each other socially for several years before we started dating and then dated seriously for another year before moving in together. After eight months, agreeing our relationship was solid, we got engaged. A year later, we married. Initially, we were very, very happy.

My family and friends liked Jonathan. They still do. There were never any red flags. I thought he was everything that mattered to me in a man and in a husband. We shared the same values and interests (except for auto racing). We came from similar backgrounds and had the same life goals. He even matched the comprehensive list of qualities I had labored over when I was still in my early twenties. He was a great guy.

We started out just fine but somehow, we didn't seem to mix well as time went on. We began bringing out the worst in each other and I was left wondering how I had managed to transform a good man into such a raving lunatic. Was it my taking up most of the closet space which finally fried him? Was it his NASCAR addiction which sent me over the edge? Let's not even get into my increasingly bad attitude or his. Let's not discuss the accusations or freezing-out silences. Even couples counseling couldn't help us reconcile or understand each other better. No real blame, though. It took both of us to come together and both of us to let go.

What did I do wrong?

As the words tumbled out, Aunt Grace sat quietly, waiting for the calm to follow and the questions that would come when the wreckage again settled. I finally ran out of words, feeling a bit battered, before asking the crucial question coming up for me again and again.

"You always say you had two great loves. We've talked about how you knew you were meant to be with each of them, but I obviously wasn't as smart as you, though I really thought I'd found my great love when I married Jonathan. I ended up feeling like a loser and very much alone. I've figured out what went wrong between us, but I don't know what to do with this new awareness. A part of me says, 'What difference would knowing make? It's not going to change anything.' But I can't believe that's true.

"I realize I must move forward, but I don't know what this means. How did you recover from the deaths of Harold and Uncle George and get on with your life? I'm really, really clueless about what to do next."

The X Factor

Grace paused a beat to be sure I had no lingering thoughts before she responded.

"Rachel, give yourself credit for how far you've come. You worked through all the emotions which kept hammering you after the divorce. As a result, you now see things more clearly and you're ready to look at your marriage more objectively. You can make different choices.

This is the next step and we'll take it together. You're doing just fine. I promise."

Mentally, the nasty nagging voice, a constant presence since the divorce was finalized, immediately retorted, "Sure—whatever you say, Aunt Grace. Like I really feel just fine, Aunt Grace. Thanks for nothing, Aunt Grace." On the outside, however, I calmly nodded like a grownup, indicating she could continue, though she must have sensed the childish diatribe and emotional foot stomping going on.

Raising an eyebrow and smiling, she hugged me briefly and stood to reopen her second suitcase. "I thought you might ask about the next step, so I picked up something for us to do over the next few days, an activity to help you sort everything out." Saying this, Grace handed me a thousand-piece jigsaw puzzle picturing the rolling hills of a countryside extravagant with wildflowers on a day of sunlight and serenity.

"This reminded me of the vacation George, you, and I took to France the summer after you graduated high school. We had such a good time and I hoped it would bring back some happy memories."

I grinned like the girl I had been just thinking about those eight weeks of exploring the country. I had briefly been to France once before, but not spent the time needed to really get to know the land and its people. I smiled even more at the memories. I had felt very grown-up and worldly traveling without my parents.

During this remarkable time, Grace and George taught me how to enjoy wonderful regional wine and food. They introduced me to the heart of France and I ended up loving it the way they did. Most importantly, they showed me how a couple could have a great time together while still maintaining their own individual identities—something, even then, I was looking for.

They were connected and independent; concerned and carefree; interested and interesting. I was able to see Grace and George's relationship with almost-adult eyes outside a child's defining context of a parental partnership. I discovered what is possible when two adults choose to be together, and I learned the important elements of good relationships just by being with them.

Pulling my mind back to the present, I looked at Grace and said with great sincerity, "France was one of the best times of my life and I still feel so lucky to have traveled with you both. But a jigsaw puzzle to get me unstuck? What are you thinking, Aunt Grace? We're talking about my life here." Yes, I got a bit snarly. She just laughed.

"I never really told a lot of people about what I did during the years after both Harold and George died. I cried a lot, slept a lot, and remembered a lot before managing to empty myself of the past—just enough to return to my emotional center where I could think more clearly about the future. After taking the time to grieve, I retreated to the beach to spend time by the ocean and figure out what to do next,

"I sat on the sand and talked to the waves, asking them to take away any emotional residue grief may have left behind. After my pain receded a little, I then invited the waves to carry in new ideas and dreams. I guess the ocean listened because once I freed up some inner space, visions of what my new future could look like eventually took shape.

"Filled with new energy and purpose, I returned to New York and worked jigsaw puzzles. Puzzles somehow helped me put together these new and unexplored possibilities and produced an image of possible next steps. Eventually, I found all the answers I needed."

"But why jigsaw puzzles? You've never mentioned them before. How does getting answers from jigsaw puzzles work?"

That's What It's All About

"You know how the brain functions. The subconscious mind works very hard at sorting information into what it knows to be *right* or *proper* categories—all the sensory data flooding us every millisecond, as well as the stream of thoughts sent from the conscious mind."

"Yes, I studied the parts and functions of the mind in school."

"Then you know when we are born, we're conditioned by our family or guardians to see and evaluate the world the way they do. They teach us what is acceptable socially, ethnically, racially, and often, religiously. These inherited, unconscious categories help us sort the brand-new experiences flooding us and essentially make sense of the world.

They allow us to integrate and belong. This conditioning process is necessary for basic survival. These right-or-proper categories remain operational until we examine them and decide for ourselves what is right and good for us. Many people unfortunately skip this crucial step.

"When this step is not taken, our experiences continue to deliver even more information to the subconscious storehouse, and the subconscious busily sorts the new material into old unexamined categories. Or, information arrives which can't be neatly slotted because this new data doesn't validate what we were originally taught. Therefore, since learned categories don't exist and different categories have not yet been developed, the subconscious cannot classify the material.

"Instead, it assigns this alien information to a *Top Secret: Do Not EVER Open* folder because, once examined, the information could produce fear, confusion, or even anger. It's dangerous—a threat to our tidy, familiar mental constructs. The new ideas might awaken us to new truth, compelling us to reshape our world view and make changes. You can understand, then, why many people unconsciously choose to stay stuck in comfortable and comforting old beliefs rather than do the inner work growth demands.

"The process of rejecting new 'secret' un-sortable information embeds inherited categories even deeper. The brain's neuropathways carrying this old material over and over again actually become more deeply grooved. Consequently, we become convinced our way of looking at things is always right and anyone not sharing our world view is wrong. Against the yardstick of our subconscious rules, we judge people, ideas, and situations. We don't even know how stuck and stunted we are."

This made total sense to me and I continued her line of reasoning.

"I always thought this sorting-into-categories process sounds like a Google search. Information is delivered matching our interests and past searches. While this might be convenient, I'm not sure it's a good thing. Same old, same old,"

"I agree. That's a helpful analogy. Our current values, attitudes, and beliefs—the drivers of our thinking, feeling, and acting in certain ways—actually emerge from these old right-or-proper categories. For the most part, the values, attitudes, and beliefs these categories end up generating are highly subjective, even those we have examined. It's simply how we work. You know the old saying, 'Birds of a feather flock together.' The same applies to people."

I smiled, saying, "And Google searches."

"Indeed. We instinctively gravitate to those who share our attitudes, beliefs, and even our opinions. The problem is, unexamined values, attitudes, and beliefs can become hard-and-fast rules and biases, and I'm sure you've met people who are driven more by their unconscious biases than by conscious values, though they believe they operate from their highest truth. People become extremists when they zealously try to convince everyone—even through violence and brain-washing—that their way is the *only* right way to live. Diverse ideas are not tolerated.

"We'd like to think we always act rationally but this simply is not true. Sometimes we have knee-jerk reactions to people or situations and act without conscious thought. The most obvious example of this is the fight-or-flight response. When we are in danger, without thinking, we automatically run away if we can—either physically or emotionally.

"At times, even when we're not in real danger, we can robotically react with like or dislike to certain people, ideas, events, and environments. Often our dislike is founded in unexamined fear arising from subconscious right-or-proper categories. A part of us becomes fearful because our world view and who we know ourselves to be are challenged. Unconsciously, we automatically shut down the perceived threat. It just happens. When it does, though, it's a good idea to later examine why we acted this way. What caused the extreme reaction? If we don't take the time to sort this out, the subconscious mind's arbitrary categories learned before we were even able to speak or think independently will continue to drive our behavior.

"As I mentioned, this early conditioning process is important and necessary for physical and psychological safety. We learn how to be part of our earliest family community. The socialization process also trains us to successfully belong to our future communities: school, work, neighborhoods, clubs, religious organizations, etc."

She paused to see if I were taking all this in.

"This makes so much sense. I sometimes think about

the judgments Jonathan and I made about each other. Where did they come from? I don't know if I ever thought about it before, so this conversation is a good one to have right now.

"However, since the rain is coming in soon, do you want to continue talking on the balcony before it starts?"

"Wonderful. Let's go. I'll get my sweater."

We walked down the short passage to the French doors opening to the second-floor balcony. The cool wind felt good on my heated face and I breathed in the moist salted air. "Let's make ourselves comfortable in these rockers, Aunt Grace. It will just take me a minute to put the seat cushions on. Can I get you anything to drink?"

"No. I can wait. Let's finish this up. I know your mother is getting lunch ready and I want to complete this conversation before then. Let's continue after you get the cushions."

We rocked quietly for a few minutes, matching the rhythms of the waves which seemed to have doubled in size since I last checked. The storm was closer than I had thought.

Chapter Three

Mysteries of the Mind

Once we were settled, Aunt Grace continued "Let's complete the right-or-proper categories. Think of them as software programs if it makes it easier. For all of us, these programs run on a common operating system called *human*. If we didn't have this common operating system, we couldn't function within the human community. If we didn't have subconscious programs, we wouldn't know how to interact with each other in order to survive and belong. Those categories— these programs—are vital.

"Now pay close attention to this next part. It's really important.

"Though we all share the same human operating system, each person's subconscious programming is unique. The programs determine how we think and feel about absolutely everything we experience. Even information coming from our senses is dependent on what we believe is important and personally meaningful.

"For example, though you and I might watch the

same sunset and agree it's beautiful, we each will actually *see* and *experience* the sunset's beauty differently because of our distinct subconscious programs. The elements of beauty pleasing to me may be different from what please you, even though we agree the shared human experience is beautiful.

"The codes for these subconscious programs, the categories we discussed, are written by our early conditioning, and afterwards, by life experiences. As we have new experiences, we assign personal meaning to them based on these programs. How you actually view your world is exclusively and irreplaceably your own.

"A sunset may be beautiful to you because the drama of contrasting colors resonates with the way you enjoy nature and observe it with an artist's eye. For me, the same sunset brings memories of my wedding ceremony. Since my marriage gave me such joy, sunsets hold happy emotional content for me. Therefore, an identical sunset; the same appreciation of beauty; but entirely different experiential responses. Are you with me so far?"

"Yes, but I still don't know how this fits into puzzling," I commented.

"Be patient. Remember when I described the first thing I did when Harold and George died? I'd first emptied myself of old emotional content in order to fill myself with new dreams and information. This is such an important first step, one I know you have already taken. For me, only after the emptying process did I feel ready to begin working my future through a jigsaw puzzle.

"I rewrote the program called *wife and partner* to bring the new program called *living by myself after death* online, essentially creating a new subconscious category. The other program remained part of my operating system, but I no longer referenced it or sorted new information into it until my life situation changed.

"Quite by accident, I realized when I work a puzzle, I am, in fact, actually delivering a message to my subconscious mind to help it sort more accurately. To be sure the message is delivered exactly as I wish, I developed a pre-puzzle practice I still follow today."

Becoming Fluent

"Since the language of the subconscious mind is written in *symbols*, then using symbols or symbolic actions within a *ritual* is fundamental, and I created one just for puzzling. First, I clearly express my intention to participate in the ritual called jigsaw puzzling and connect more precisely with my subconscious mind. I then direct my subconscious to put all the information spinning around inside me into some kind of order based upon the attitudes, values, and beliefs I have examined and consciously made my own.

"I state that just as I take the many different puzzle pieces and form them into a pattern, I expect my subconscious mind to reveal life patterns I will understand from the information filling me. I clearly tell this part of my mind to deliver new understanding to the conscious mind either during the puzzle process itself or a few days after the puzzle is completed. Then I relax and simply let my subconscious do its behind-the-scenes work and settle happily into working the puzzle. I follow the same process today.

"Throughout the puzzling process, I remain confident I'll receive my answers by the time I've finished the puzzle or soon after. When I complete it, the patterns formed by my subconscious automatically show up in my conscious mind, and these patterns eventually lead me to the answers I need.

"However, I always first examine these answers for appropriateness and fit with my *chosen* attitudes, values, and beliefs, just to be sure I'm not fooling myself. If everything checks out with *both* my head and my heart, then I act on them. In all the years I've been working puzzles, I can honestly say this ritual has never failed as long as I follow every step and confidently expect my stated outcomes to be delivered."

I was rocking furiously at this point, listening intently, and once again interrupted her. "Are you saying by doing a jigsaw puzzle I can all get the answers I need to move on with my life? Could any kind of puzzle or game work the same way?"

"Let me answer your last question first. I like to do jigsaw puzzles because they slow me down and completely redirect my conscious attention for the length of time my subconscious needs to do its work. But I think any puzzle or game—any paper, table-top, or electronic game—focusing the mind on either problem-solving or on the manipulation of diverse pieces to form patterns—anything slowing the conscious mind down—can apply the ritual of puzzling.

"I've also read *thinking and feeling* while concurrently *doing* something with our hands makes a stronger impression on the brain than just doing it. Therefore, I mesh thinking and feeling into puzzling as well. I think about the end result and how wonderful I will feel when the puzzle process delivers information about my goal. I visualize the end result using all my senses. I see it, hear it, smell it, sense it, and taste it until my new future becomes real to me in the present moment. Therefore, you might visualize how your life will look when you finally integrate this difficult experience and begin feeling right now how happy you will be when you finally move on.

"On the other hand, being mindless—not focusing on any conscious thoughts and simply enjoying the puzzle experience—also allows the subconscious mind to work beneficially if we enter this no-mind state with conscious intention. Either approach works and can change as the purpose for working a puzzle changes.

"I've found a puzzle type involving physical manipulation gives me easier access to my subconscious mind. Everyone is unique, though, and different types of puzzles attract different types of people according to how they retrieve their internal information. Jigsaw puzzles work for me because I enjoy the quiet concentration of working them, as interesting scenes slowly unfold when I fit more puzzle pieces together.

However, jigsaw puzzling might not work for everyone. Each person must find his or her own way into the subconscious mind."

Just a Reminder

"Now to answer your first question. I will answer this quickly since we're both probably getting hungry.

"Yes, I know absolutely you can get the answers you need by working a puzzle—in this case, a jigsaw puzzle. However, remember that in order to get the full benefit from puzzling, a few things must first happen.

"As I've outlined, you need to take the all-important step of letting go any strong emotions still tying you to the past, and then once emptied, filling yourself again with new thoughts, desires, and dreams. This doesn't mean letting go your past entirely—just releasing the constricting emotions holding you to a time now over. From talking to you during the last several months, it seems to me like you've taken these two steps. Am I correct?"

"I believe I have. Good Lord, I hope I have. I would never want to go through that again." I almost shuddered thinking about it.

"After the divorce was finalized, I took a week off work and allowed myself to break open and just grieve—to scream and shout and cry as every possible memory and emotion swamped me. It wasn't pretty. I was a mess. But I took the time to be with whatever feelings came up, just as you suggested. It was hard work, but I stayed with it. I wouldn't let any feeling go until I knew I was done with it, scrubbing myself clean of any emotional scum which could later grow like toxic mold in the darkness of my subconscious. I knew it could even eventually make me sick.

"By the end of the week, I passed through the worst part of my raw grief and went back to work, though I remained vigilant for sneak attacks. As the weeks went by, when I least expected them, feelings would jump out of hiding, trying to tackle me and bring me down. Though the mourning process continued, as I handled the hard stuff coming up, every day got easier. You were a lifesaver in getting me through those early days and I'll always be totally grateful to you.

"After the initial grieving was over—once I felt like I'd emptied myself of dreary thoughts and negative feelings—I spent a number of weekends here at the shore with my parents and walked or ran for hours. Gus loved it and thought I was visiting just for his amusement.

"I took the time to look at whatever new thoughts and insights popped into my head. I also paid more attention to the happier memories of Jonathan and my marriage. By doing this, I managed to forgive both him and myself. Mom and Dad were really supportive and very patient throughout this period and left me alone when I wanted to be alone and were there when I needed them.

"For the no-mind creative process you recommended, since Jonathan had already moved out, I filled an entire wall of the living room with finger-paint paper and smeared it with whatever colors felt right. At one point, I covered myself with finger paint and rubbed different parts of my body against the paper. Very interesting results. I would highly recommend the process.

"I forgot how freeing it is to just play with colors without trying to draw something recognizable. This exercise generated a lot of new ideas and I found even my dreaming became more colorful. I began feeling hopeful again, but recently I've gotten stuck. What the heck, Aunt Grace?

"I did all the inner work you suggested, but nothing seems to be happening. I'm at a standstill. I know it's been only a few months since the divorce, but I believe I should be further along in the healing process. I don't know what else to do with myself. Ugh. I'm getting whiney."

Aunt Grace smiled and squeezed my hand. "You aren't whiney. You're just being human, and you simply need to get past this and move forward again. It's why I brought along a jigsaw puzzle for just the two of us. You've done your inner work. You've let go of the negative charge on many of your constricting emotions and can focus now on more positive, expansive ones.

"You've gathered all these new ideas and potential dreams about what the future can hold. It's now time to direct your subconscious to put the information together into helpful patterns to consciously find the answers you need. Are you up to learning the ritual of jigsaw puzzling? Once you practice it, you can apply the ritual to any kind of puzzle; relate it to any process you're working with; and use it for whatever you're struggling with in life."

"Absolutely! Maybe we can take a walk on the beach after lunch before the storm arrives and begin the puzzle afterwards."

As if on cue, my mother came upstairs to tell us lunch was ready. I followed the two of them as they chatted about Grace's upcoming party on Saturday. Mom had made arrangements with a local restaurant to host the dinner party in their large banquet room stretching far into the ocean, and Dad hired a band known for playing the kind of music Grace enjoyed. The restaurant offered a gorgeous backdrop for the event, and drinks and hors d'oeuvres would be served during sunset. The imminent nor'easter was predicted to blow itself out by Friday morning and, consequently, the sky would be scoured clean and ready to put on a show.

About a hundred people were coming from all over to celebrate with Grace, and I looked forward to seeing all her friends again. The drive for most of the guests from nearby cities was not a long one, and a ferry ran regularly from New York to our town. Many local friends would find it easy to attend while those more distant would arrive by plane or train.

Grace Prepares to Shift My World

We had a bracing fall lunch of soup, salad, and sandwiches while Grace regaled us with stories of her extended stay in central Italy with Antonio. Three generations of his family lived in or around the compound, and Grace had a wonderful time visiting with all of them. They seemed to be everywhere. Seven generations had worked this land, so they had found plenty of time to reproduce.

Mom asked her what she enjoyed most about the vineyard. Aunt Grace responded by vividly describing the fragrance of grapes warming in the sun, the scent filling the house as the day grew hotter. Literally indescribable. Then she told us about several events hosted in their honor with lots of eating and dancing. I could tell she missed Antonio, but he had business in the city and would not arrive until Saturday morning.

He's another one who hasn't slowed down, and I know Aunt Grace finds this very attractive. Someone to keep up with her! To give Antonio a chance to enjoy the shore, the two of them would remain for a week following the party when the rest of us went home.

She was so full of life and as I listened, the only word pinging my mind was *remarkable*. Grace defied the current paradigm of aging and was growing older in her own way. She remained a beautiful and elegant woman with a subtle sense of humor helping her see life as something to be explored and enjoyed rather than a burden to be endured. Yes, she had slowed down, but she had not come close to stopping. She certainly was resetting my own thoughts about getting older. Mom has said the same thing.

After lunch, Grace went upstairs to change her shoes and get a jacket. The beach could be chilly in October, especially with the wind gusting as it was. I loved the beach at all times of the year and in any kind of weather. Grace did too.

I was fortunate to have spent a lot of time at the shore in northern New Jersey within commuting distance of New York, and I had the security of knowing I could always come home no matter where life took me. This home was my refuge.

The farmhouse-style house is a rambling two-story structure with wide verandas wrapping around the entire ground floor and balconies across the front and back of the second. I loved the dark gray siding, white trim, and black shutters. The pop of deep red on the front door always makes me smile when I approach it.

The house is situated on the large lot with a slight incline, boundaried by tall pine and red oak trees which have survived many storms and even a few hurricanes. The house has high ceilings, hardwood floors, lots of fireplaces, ornamental wood details, and several stained-glass windows. I especially enjoy all the sounds it makes—the creaks and squeaks of an older home. It speaks! Every time I walk in, I can feel the house hugging me, welcoming me home.

Grace had announced our puzzle event at lunch, and Dad said he would set up a table in the front sunroom where we could puzzle in front of a fire while enjoying the ocean. Grace checked the table's size; declared it large enough; and asked Dad to place two comfortable chairs on either side. When all was arranged to her satisfaction, we bundled up and walked across the street to the beach, following the path through the dunes.

Gus had rushed to the beach and was already on the other side of the dunes, but we could track him through his barking and high-flying tail. A colony of seagulls rose screeching. Grace and I just looked at each other and smiled. "Gus!" we both said at the same time.

"The *third* step of puzzling is as important as the first and second," Grace said.

"The *third* step? What happened to the first two?"

"I already took care of the *second* step at lunch when I told those who would be around the puzzle—your parents—that only the two of us could work on it. This is our project—our process—so it's important to establish puzzle boundaries up front. If you're working a puzzle by yourself, you need to make clear to anyone coming into your home the puzzle is off-limits to them. This may sound like a small point, but it has huge implications.

"Unless you clearly set your boundaries with others, you cannot complain when they breach them. This is true in life as well as puzzling, by the way. You'll be amazed by how people automatically sit down to work a puzzle when they see it on a table. People like puzzles because we're all natural problem-solvers.

"If you find you're uncomfortable setting puzzle boundaries, examine other life boundaries you may be ignoring or have trouble setting. Your discomfort could point to some inner work you need to do."

She laughed when she saw my frown. "Sorry, Rachel, but there's always something in puzzling and in life to pay attention to." Then she continued discussing the puzzle process.

"The actual *first* step of the puzzling process is choosing a puzzle which pleases you. You did this when you approved the puzzle I brought with me. When I purchased it, I thought you might enjoy working on something to touch your heart and bring back happy memories. However, there are many jigsaw puzzle choices depending on what you need the subconscious to do.

"Sometimes I choose puzzles with all my favorite colors because working on them would make me happy. Or, if I need some quick answers, I purchase a puzzle with only several hundred pieces I can put together in a few hours. At other times, I want to spend time in the puzzle space, so I buy a fifteen-hundred-piece puzzle I know will take days to finish. If I really want to challenge myself because I'm reaching for an out-of-the-box solution, I look for a difficult puzzle with predominately one color. There are even three-dimensional puzzles to work on several levels.

"My puzzle choice, then, is determined by the information I'm going after. If I'm working on business issues, I find a puzzle to engage my mind or pique my curiosity. If I'm working on personal or emotional issues, I buy a puzzle to move my heart. The trick is to listen to how you feel. Allow your intuition to guide you to exactly the right puzzle.

"This process is what I call the *Zen of Puzzles*—the ability to be fully present and listen closely to what is needed in order to respond with integrity. Doing this in right timing offers *aha moments* of awakening and understanding (if we choose to accept them), delivered not through the mind's logic but through the heart's knowing. It takes practice, but the effort is well worth it.

"For you, I thought it was important to involve your heart, so I purchased the puzzle I showed you. Since you now know about this important step, would you rather look for another?"

"No! I absolutely love this one. It's perfect. As I said, it reminds me of a very happy time in my life, and I couldn't think of a better way to reveal the patterns of my new future. Now what about the *third* step you mentioned?"

What? There's More?

Before answering, Aunt Grace glanced at the sky and noticed the wind had picked up and the sky was getter much darker. I looked up and saw Gus still tearing along the beach so I called him back. It was time to make the turn towards home.

"The *third* step," Grace repeated, though she grimaced a little before replying. "Well, this is a bit of a hot button for me. So many people *dream* big dreams and never give themselves the space to *live* their big dreams. They don't take risks; they play it safe; they stay with what is comfortable and familiar while complaining nothing interesting ever happens to them or nothing ever changes.

"We completed the *third* puzzle step when I confirmed the puzzle table was large enough to work the puzzle comfortably. Since the table is a metaphor for creating a platform in life on which to build our dreams, the choice of table is also an important ritual signaling the subconscious mind we have provided enough space for new life patterns to more readily show up. To continue this analogy.

"I believe these dream-big/work-small people put the big puzzle pieces of their dreams on a tiny table fashioned by the pre-programmed experiences they allow themselves to have. They automatically restrict their possibilities by limiting the size of their life's platform. Their work surfaces are just too contained, so their human potential may never be fully realized. Essentially, these people set themselves up for failure from the get-go. The pieces of their life's puzzle never form the picture they want because they don't give themselves the space needed to grow and change.

"When I'm working a puzzle, I give my subconscious mind the message it has lots of room to maneuver and I'm willing to go outside the known boundaries of my comfort zone to broaden my perspective. Therefore, I always choose a table with six or more inches of space around the puzzle for moving pieces to different spots and working on different sections. Picking the right table—like picking the rightly proportioned platform for the life you want to create—is an important part of the puzzle ritual."

My eyebrows were now somewhere near the top of my forehead. "Good grief. I never thought working a jigsaw puzzle or any puzzle, to be honest, could show me so much about my life and the way I'm approaching it. This has been your big secret all along? This is your big reveal?"

Grace twinkled back, "Oh, this is just one of my secrets, but using puzzling to work through a complex issue with great intention is an important skill I've developed over the years. I never really mentioned puzzling before because it's only recently I've been able to put words around what I've instinctively been doing for decades. I didn't frame puzzling in the context of a ritual until a few years ago, and I never thought the process was something I would teach others—until now, that is." We were both quiet as I took this in.

I could see our home in the distance. Good thing, since the rising wind was tossing loose sand around. Gus ran up and diligently sniffed the ground in front of us as if, in his doggy way, he was trying to keep us safe from hidden landmines. He even dug a few holes just to be sure we would be okay. Gus, our guardian and protector.

Then I asked, "Since you've now figured this out, why don't you write a book about puzzling? It seems to me a lot of people would love to learn about how something this simple can be used so profoundly."

"I'm not interested in writing a book, but if you want to develop one after we complete the puzzle, be my guest. You can even take notes while we're working."

"It's a deal. Though I'll probably record our conversations to make it easier for me to be accurate, if it's okay with you. You tell me your puzzling secrets and I'll make you famous. *The Secrets of Grace, the Great Puzzle Master.* How does the title sound?"

We both laughed and continued walking arm-in-arm, thinking of everything we had talked about. Since we were getting closer to the house, Grace slowed her pace a little and said, "Now you're ready for the *fourth* step in the puzzle ritual—giving directions to your subconscious mind. You need to be very clear about what you want to achieve when working the puzzle by using unambiguous words to frame your intentions.

"Tell your subconscious mind you will soon be working a puzzle to help you understand your future life patterns more clearly. Ask for its cooperation in putting these patterns together for you during the puzzle process and while you're sleeping. Then thank your subconscious mind in advance for supporting your work. You can say all this mentally, but it's much more powerful to speak it out loud. Hearing your own words will make a deeper impression on both your conscious and subconscious minds.

"You can light a candle or play special music as part of your ritual, if you wish. But for now, I'm going to talk to my subconscious as we walk the rest of the way to the house. Then, when I go to my bedroom, I'll repeat both my intention and request out loud. You might want do this as well." I did.

We walked in silence having important conversations with our subconscious minds. The sun came out briefly and shot light onto the ocean making the water spark with thousands of pinpoint lights. Gus made a final lunge at the seagulls and chased them until they gave up and flew away. Other small white-and-gray shore birds foraged at water's edge like squadrons of hyperactive angels. I took this as a good sign.

Silently, I spoke to my subconscious mind, asking for help; explaining what I needed; and thanking it in advance for its cooperation. Step *four* was almost complete. All that remained was speaking the words out loud and I would be ready to work the puzzle. I would be ready to engage the next phase of my life.

Chapter Four

The Beginning

When we got back, we sat and enjoyed a cup of tea with Mom and spent a comfortable hour swapping stories. Dad was outside doing something mysterious to buttress the back fence before the storm hit. Gus rushed to help but quickly abandoned him to come inside and flop in front of the fire. He was exhausted. His bravery tested by many imagined beach dangers, he had emerged unbowed and victorious. Gus felt fully justified in lowering his guard and falling soundly asleep. We were all safe.

Afterwards, Grace went upstairs for some quiet time before dinner and I gave Mom a reprieve from cooking. I enjoyed cooking, especially for my family, and I intended to spoil them and myself as much as possible while we were together.

As I readied everything, I thought about using the puzzling ritual to access the subconscious mind. The idea of doing something fun to accomplish a serious goal was rather perfect. Simply directing my subconscious mind to deliver information I needed? What a cool concept! The subconscious for me was still a big mystery—an iceberg-like part of the mind staying mostly hidden beneath the surface, ready to either guide me or sink me.

I knew a huge amount of data was stored there if I could just figure out how to retrieve it. My mother had taught my brother and me that all the answers we would ever need were already inside us. She told us to practice finding our quiet inner voice and listening to what it said. (Robert and I later argued about what the voice sounded like. As the older brother, he said his voice probably sounded much smarter than mine and, therefore, I should always listen to what he had to say. Nice try, Robert.)

Mom cautioned us never to pay attention to the shrill, nagging voice also inside us, scolding and raising fears, and assured us we would know the difference between the two. The quiet voice would make us feel steady and calm, but the Nag, as she dubbed it, would make us feel lousy. (I told Robert I thought the voice he was listening to was the Nag since it sounded so much like him. He was not amused.)

Over the past several months, I had certainly become reacquainted with the Nag. I began to better understand what Mom had meant after talking about this voice with Grace.

Puzzles, Puzzles Everywhere

While I prepared to cook, I thought about what I was doing, the steps I was taking—gathering different foods and putting them together to concoct a meal. But wasn't this exactly like putting a puzzle together? Couldn't I ask my subconscious to help me as I cooked a meal if I needed a quick hit of information? I made a mental note to ask Aunt Grace.

My father shot through the mudroom door bringing the first splashes of rain with him. Dad's eyes lit up when he saw me kneading dough for bread. He is so predictable and easy to please, and it doesn't take much to make him happy. I made fresh coffee and watched as he poured a cup before sitting at the kitchen table to talk.

"How are you doing, honey? I haven't had a chance to talk to you since you arrived yesterday."

"I'm doing better now I'm with all of you. Work has been really busy. It seems like everyone came down with a nasty bug once school started and the number of prescriptions has spiked. I was glad to get this week off and I was excited when Mom said the two of you took off as well. When do you need to go back to work?"

"Not until Monday afternoon, so I'll be home the entire time you're here. I must be in the office next Wednesday for a few big clients coming to discuss some contract issues, but I'll be back here full-time on Thursday to visit with Aunt Grace. She looks really good, don't you think?"

"She looks great. When I was walking with her on the beach, I couldn't believe how strong she is and how far she wanted to go. I think I was more tired than she was by the time we got back. Did Aunt Grace tell you what we'll be doing with the puzzle?"

"No. Tell me."

We had a fascinating conversation about how the mind worked, and my father gave me examples of how his legal work was like a puzzle he put together. He explained how often, after working on a case for a while without a clear direction, he would unexpectedly wake up one morning with the answer he'd been looking for. This happened so regularly, he kept his cell phone near his bed to record his thoughts when he woke up. To me, it certainly sounded like the subconscious operating. Dad said he also got another idea about accessing the subconscious from Henry Francis DuPont.

"This particular DuPont of the famous DuPont family was actually a horticulturist and one of the premier US breeders of Holstein Friesian cattle. On his tax returns, he identified himself as a farmer and lived on the beautiful Winterthur estate outside Wilmington, Delaware where he was born. We took you there when you were younger, but you should really go again the next time you visit your brother. It's not too far from Philadelphia and has stunning gardens and grounds.

"On the tour of the estate home, the docent explained that after lunch, DuPont would sit in a comfortable chair holding a stone in each hand placed directly over pie tins.

After relaxing, he'd let himself doze lightly to access the creative state between waking and sleeping. As he started to fall asleep, his hands grew limp; the rocks dropped and hit the pie tins; and he immediately returned to full wakefulness. DuPont then wrote down whatever he remembered from his almost-asleep state where he said he had received some of his best ideas. I never forgot the story and tried it myself. Like anything, it takes practice, but it works."

"Wow, Dad, how amazing is that? I love the idea! I don't remember hearing this part when we were on the tour, but I might have been too engrossed looking at all the gorgeous antiques, another thing he was known for. And you're right. I need to get back there. Thank you!"

I told him my most recent thoughts about cooking as a type of puzzle. We both agreed no matter what we were doing, the practice of living more consciously and mindfully was a very good idea. After his second cup of coffee, Dad gave me a big hug and went upstairs to take a shower before dinner. I put the finishing touches on the meal before getting wine and munchies ready for the all-important, before-dinner part of any significant gathering.

I brought everything into the living room and built up the fire again. Gus grunted his gratitude and rolled over to warm his other side. The rain which had announced itself earlier arrived in torrents, and wind screamed through the trees. The nor'easter arrived in grand style and I was more than ready to curl up and watch the almost-hurricane push through the neighborhood. I loved hearing the rain pound on the roof and drum the windows. To me, this was the best time to be at the shore, and I could feel my heart marinating in peace. I was caught up in profound gratitude.

As I sat in front of the fire with these people I loved, I totally understood the term *Happy Hour.* Gathering at the end of the day was a special ritual for closing it out properly—talking and laughing; drinking and enjoying appetizers; swapping stories both funny and profound; appreciating time together in the present to distill fond memories for the future. Life was good indeed.

Talking about the Absent

Conversation turned to Robert and his family. He married fairly young the summer between graduating university and joining the Air Force, but had made a fortunate choice of wife. Gina was vivacious and smart, a good complement to my more serious brother. She was a wonderful wife and mother, totally devoted to their three children. I was clueless about how she managed a full-time job as a daytime chef given her hectic family schedule, especially since Robert flew commercial jets with all too frequent last-minute schedule changes.

Fortunately, Gina worked in her family's restaurant and could manage her calendar as the week demanded, but everything she juggled must be a big stretch. I really loved my sister-in-law and saw how much she lightened up my straight-arrow brother.

They were having a hard time with their oldest child, Elizabeth, who was once the sweetest girl on the planet but after adolescent hormones kicked in, she was now more like a shrew on steroids. Elizabeth (who used to be Beth until she insisted on being called by her more grown-up name) was only fourteen, and they still had a long road to travel with her. We all looked forward to the return of our Beth (or her own version of the matured Elizabeth).

It was a good thing the next-in-line, Jeffrey, had not yet succumbed to adolescent angst. However, since he had just turned eleven, his time was drawing near, and Gina and Robert were warily watching for signs of onset derangement. Jeffrey was a happy, balanced kid with even odds he would navigate *the emotional makeover* (as his parents euphemistically termed adolescence) more smoothly. He was a self-proclaimed certified geek and reveled in all things digital. Jeffrey was a real cyber cutie and I trusted he would stay that way during his hormonal surge.

Sammy was my godson and I thought he was just perfect. Not that I didn't love the other two just as much, but Sammy held a special place in my heart. He was nine and the dreamer of the family. He saw into the hearts of everything and everyone, and managed to convey his deep sensibilities through music. Sammy played the piano beautifully, though, on balance, he also excelled at baseball and track. A great setup for an emerging Renaissance man. It would be fun to see how his life unfolded.

Happy hour became two hours. Happy thoughts. Happy times. I really looked forward to seeing Robert and Gina on Friday. They were giving themselves some adult space and coming to the party by themselves. Then the entire family would return the following weekend to give the children some Aunt Grace Time. They would all have a ridiculously fun time—even Elizabeth—especially Elizabeth.

Robert and Gina's children loved and deeply appreciated their Great-Great-Aunt and regularly wrote about her for school assignments. When he was six, much to her delight, Sammy invited Aunt Grace to school to be his show-and-tell for the topic, *the most interesting person you know.* I was not the least bit disappointed he didn't ask me to be his visual aide because I would have picked Grace as well.

On Friday, Gina planned to pick up the three from school at 2:00 and deliver them to her sister's house to spend the weekend with their two cousins. Afterwards, she and Robert would meet and drive up together, hopefully beating most of the traffic and arriving by early evening. Though the two-hour drive from Philadelphia was relatively easy, they would probably run into some traffic. We told them not to worry about keeping to a schedule since I would have a crock-pot meal ready when they arrived.

After enjoying drinks in front of the fire, we moved to the dining room for dinner. I must say, the meal was delicious. I smiled when I noticed the entire loaf of bread disappearing at Dad's end of the table despite my mother's meaningful looks my father just as meaningfully ignored.

Since I could predict his hangdog look when he realized the bread was gone, I preempted his whimpers by letting him know I had made a second loaf for the morning. He sighed blissfully. Familiar with this particular sigh, Mom did her own preempting and said he could not eat the second loaf as dessert. However, I was not surprised when I later went into the kitchen to find a big hunk was missing.

Beginning to Begin

My father cleaned up while my mother, Aunt Grace, and I enjoyed Irish coffee in front of the fire, the perfect beverage for a blustery evening. Afterwards, Grace and I went into the sunroom to set up the puzzle for the next day. During our beach walk, Grace had explained she liked doing this preparation ahead of time to become familiar with the puzzle before actually working on it. She wanted to touch each puzzle piece and look at all its colors. By doing this, she explained, her subconscious mind could *register* the pieces and begin the sifting and sorting process while she slept.

Grace asked me to open the puzzle box and pour the pieces onto the table. Then she said, "Remember the saying, *Well begun is half done?*" The expression must be one of those generational things because I honestly could not say I had heard it, but I did get the point. She continued.

"Watch people when they begin a new task if you want to understand how their minds work. Those who get the most done typically are the best organized. They take the time to arrange everything in advance and when they finally put their full attention on the job, whatever they need to perform the task is ready. They don't need to keep jumping up and down to get things they forgot.

"If you put 50% of your energy into getting organized up front, you still have 50% left to complete your project. This is all you actually need. Those who don't plan waste their energy. They dive right into a project and use 100% for the *doing*, often running out of energy before completing the task. They used 50% of what could have been their planning energy to correct mistakes; change their original concept; or gather information, people, or items they failed to consider before they got started.

"The end result is typically not very good and in order to make it right, they rework parts of the project and spend double the time and energy. This has happened to us both when we rushed into something too quickly only to regret later our lack of initial thought and preparation. We see evidence of this all the time in people around us, especially when they're very stressed. Since I don't believe in wasting either my time or my energy, for me, advance planning is key.

"I noticed you planned ahead when you were getting ready to cook. You measured and chopped your ingredients and gathered everything you'd need when you actually started cooking. As you know, this is called *mise en place,* the methodology used in all professional kitchens. It saves time and energy, especially in a fast-paced, high-stress environment. If all projects were approached with mise-en-place thinking, they would go much more easily."

Gus wandered in and looked at me pleadingly. I knew his looks and excused myself for a minute to build a fire—a great idea on a stormy day. Smart dog. Fireplaces were in almost all the living spaces, yet another reason to love this house.

Gus watched gratefully, licked my hand three times, and turned around twice before curling up and sighing blissfully when the fire grew. Another easy-to-please family member. I closed the screen and returned my attention to Aunt Grace.

"Gus is happy so now you can continue."

"While you were building the fire, I thought of an example about advance preparation. The last time I attended a meeting for my foundation, the committee discussed the annual fundraising event. The event coordinator had just gone out on maternity leave and though she had left detailed notes, we were short-staffed. When the meeting began, instead of appointing someone to moderate the discussion, everyone just threw out ideas, and we ended up making very little progress. I decided to take over and set the meeting's direction.

"By the end of the meeting, we had defined action steps and the person responsible for executing each; a timeline; a periodic reporting structure to keep us on track; and a contingency plan to handle unforeseen issues. Spending planning time up front ensured that the event would take place the way we wanted. Have you found this to be true for you?"

I told her about a few times when things went a lot easier with proper planning and other times when events imploded either because I had not considered key elements in advance or, in initial discussions, not included everyone who might be impacted. These forgotten folks naturally became annoyed (or worse) at being overlooked and it took twice as much effort to get them on board. Once Aunt Grace was sure I understood her point, she applied it to the puzzle process.

"As you would do for any project, you need to make a good beginning with your puzzle. You don't want to be careless and unwittingly give your subconscious the message it will be okay to hand you sloppy results at the end of this project. You must be precise. Here is how I suggest we begin."

Grace took me through her sorting process, the *fifth* step of puzzling.

"Sort the pieces by general color range, pulling out all the border pieces with a straight edge. Some puzzle types could have round border pieces, and more challenging puzzles might not even have a defined border.

"Within each color range, group the pieces more finely by either color gradation or similar graphic pattern. Pieces could also be grouped by their shape once you sort them by color and pattern. In the beginning, you can skip this step and use it when fewer pieces remain.

"Assemble the border. If a few pieces are missing even after you've looked through the color groups, then begin working the puzzle. Later, you will either find the missing

pieces or realize that border pieces you've already placed
must be repositioned.

"For easy placement, move the color groups near the
part of the border most similar in color and pattern."

It took a little time to group the pieces to Grace's
satisfaction. When I failed to be precise enough, she
reminded me "Well begun is half done, Rachel." Okay.
Okay. Now that I knew what she meant, I focused on
being more meticulous.

In the Good Old Days

While we were sorting, Grace began talking about interlocking puzzle pieces.

"Puzzles used to have true interlocking pieces. You
could pick up an entire completed section, and the pieces
would stay together without falling apart. This is not true
for many of the puzzles today. The pieces themselves tend
to be thinner and many do not lock into place.

"Therefore, you will find that some pieces initially
fitting together end up being joined with other pieces.
The only way to figure out a piece's right placement
is to keep working on the section until it eventually
becomes clear whether a piece is a true fit. It's like
doing a crossword puzzle and entering a word you're
not sure about. Later, when this word is crossed by a
second and third word you *are* absolutely certain of,
you'll know right away whether you need to change
the first word.

"I hear people say jigsaw puzzles have become cheaper, less finely crafted, because pieces don't lock together. I disagree. To me, today's puzzles mirror real life more accurately. Here's how I apply this non-interlocking concept.

"As I have new experiences, I search for their meaning. Then I play with the meaning and keep moving it around in my mind and heart to see how it fits into my life's patterns. This process is similar to what I do when I'm moving puzzle pieces around, trying to find their patterns.

"If the meaning I attached to my experience seems to align with my core pattern, the values and beliefs I hold as absolutely true for me, I then examine the new experience from all angles and decide if I want to integrate it with my core. I add it if I believe it will make a positive difference. If it won't, I then discard it or give it a different meaning, either immediately or over time, as I become clearer about who I am and what I want.

"This is not a once-and-done process because *I* am never done growing and changing and can never become once-and-done. The picture of my life keeps reworking itself as I gather more life experiences which shift or refine my perspective. This is what growth is all about.

"Even when I add new pieces to enhance my core pattern, because they don't interlock, it's actually easier to change my mind about them later as I gain further clarity. I can do a better job of accurately moving meaningful experiences to another place in my larger pattern or even decide to eliminate them. This is exactly like working today's puzzles.

"Puzzle pieces must be examined; checked for fit; and discarded if they don't connect. Similarly, aspects of your life will either remain or be removed the more insights you gain through people and events. The larger patterns always shift with the living of life if you remain conscious and take full responsibility for everything you do. If you try to lock in satisfying parts to keep them from changing, you stop growing. Anyway, not changing is an impossible pursuit. It simply won't happen.

"Also, interlocking puzzle pieces created an illusion of control. Every piece fit precisely into another piece, and only one piece was the exact fit for another. The pieces were pre-cut this way. No deviations. Of course, you could try to force-fit a piece by not paying attention or placing one not following the puzzle pattern.

"With today's puzzles, however, there are surprises. The puzzle piece you initially thought would fit might eventually end up moving to another place. You might have three possible placement options for just one puzzle piece. Isn't this really a more realistic metaphor for the way life works? Isn't it better to know what is true for you and then build around that truth to reframe your perspective? Isn't it more interesting to be surprised by different possibilities rather than living in the dullness of controlled sameness?"

With Eyes Wide Open and Mouth Agape

I was dumbfounded. All this wisdom embodied in puzzling? Who knew? We were only at the beginning of our puzzling experience and already I had a lot to think about. How in the world did she figure out all these life lessons just by working jigsaw puzzles? Puzzling was certainly going to be interesting, and I suspected I was in for a ride. I better get new batteries for the recorder and begin journaling my thoughts!

A huge gust of wind blew down the chimney and sparks snapped against the fire screen. Gus woke up and barked at it before, rather annoyed, he left to return to the living room.

Aunt Grace and I looked at each other and laughed. She concluded the evening by talking about individual puzzle pieces.

"Honor each puzzle piece as you would honor every event of your life. Hold it; sit with it; see what it wants to say to you. By doing this, you become intimate with the puzzle and it will actually begin to work with you.

"As you stand in the question of where a piece belongs in the puzzle, be willing to be wrong about its placement. Don't engage the puzzle with certitude. Let it unfold for you and, again, allow surprises. Never force a puzzle piece.

"It's easy to see how you can apply this to your current life. You're not sure what your next steps should be right now. Just hold the question inside you with patience and compassion. The answers will come, but you cannot force them.

"Life is not about always having the right answers. It's about knowing you're doing the best you can with the information you have while remaining confident more understanding will follow. Let this be true for you and let it be okay. Be willing to be wrong and trust your process. Your right direction will naturally reveal itself if you hold onto what is right for you.

"All living things—and remember change is a living energy—have their own gestation period. An expectant mother knows her child will be born in its own time, understanding that the exact gestation period is different for each child. Trust your own gestation period, Rachel. It is giving you time to prepare for the coming changes.

"Keep moving. Take small steps. Try things out. Changing your mind about a direction actually lets your subconscious know you're not stuck and you're ready to move on. Don't worry about altering your course right now. Everything will become clearer with time.

"Getting back to the puzzle. By consciously working with the puzzle this way—being willing to be wrong about a piece's placement in order to finally find the right one—you send a signal to your subconscious. You put it on notice that just as you consciously work the puzzle with respect, honoring yourself and your process is how you choose to live *all* the time.

"If you are consistent and steadfast, the subconscious will rewrite your old software programs to line up with this new choice. Let a puzzle be your teacher. When you approach it as a micro-process with clear intent, you can become proficient in the art of macro-living. You need to have a lot of practice and an abundance of patience, but knowing you, you'll do just fine. You've always been a quick study.

"Let's stop for tonight. We have the border completed and the pieces initially sorted. Each piece has been touched. Remember you cannot complete the whole puzzle if even one small piece is missing. This is true for your life as well.

"Whether you understand it or not, my darling Rachel, you cannot live your life in fullness and wholeness without embracing every single one of the experiences which have essentially made you who you are today—experiences trivial and profound, light and dark, happy and sad. I quite like who you are today, and I like the woman you continue to become. Keep holding on dearly to each piece of your life whether you have found a place for it yet or not. Like a puzzle piece, it's an important part of your life's picture when viewed in its wholeness."

Hundreds of thoughts fought for my attention, and I literally could not speak. Grace took one last look at me and chuckled. She kissed the top of my head; said good night; and went up the stairs. Her final direction to me was to remind my subconscious before I went to sleep about what I wanted from the puzzling process and to thank it in advance for its help.

I stayed just a few more minutes staring at the puzzle before I turned off the lights; closed the fireplace flue; said goodnight to my parents; scratched Gus in his favorite spot; and went upstairs to my bedroom. I pulled out my journal and wrote a summary of the first five steps of the puzzle process and my impression of each. As much as I could, I tried to capture Grace's insights and what they meant to me, though I was very glad I had recorded the conversation. There was a lot to take in.

After journaling, I turned off the light and sat on the window seat to watch the storm. It was a big one and already the generator had kicked in when the power went out a few hours after dinner. I opened my heart and let in everything Aunt Grace had said before allowing all thoughts to slip away, just enjoying the gift of this storm.

When I started to nod, I changed my clothes and climbed into bed, reading briefly before settling for sleep. I remembered to do as Grace suggested and talked to my subconscious. The scientific part of me felt a bit guilty, like I was cheating on the medical community. Quite honestly, my conscious mind wondered what kind of Alice-in-Wonderland rabbit hole I had fallen through.

During the night I dreamed of puzzle pieces chasing me down the path to the March Hare's tea party. I blamed the Irish coffee.

Chapter Five

Putting It All Together

After my initial psychedelic, dropped-into-Wonderland dreams, I slept soundly. Afterwards, though I couldn't recall having any mind-blowing sleep adventures, I did wake up feeling centered and excited about the day ahead.

It was still very early and the rain, just a streaming mist. Knowing this slight break would not last long, I put on my running shoes, softly called Gus, and headed to the beach. I stood and looked over the ocean, huge waves racing each other to the shore. The normally placid water was muscled with pumped-up curves.

Stretching while Gus danced around trying to lick my face, I began a slow jog, gradually picking up speed and running without much thought. Gus chased every shore bird daring to cross his path.

I enjoyed being outdoors again, dewed with mist and peppered with seafoam. Gus tried to eat it.

The sky was still a pre-dawn, gunmetal gray and I was careful not to trip on the driftwood or squash through the seaweed littering the beach after last night's high tide. Gus, however, rushed to roll in the piles of sea-stuff, paws waving in the air; tongue flopping sideways; grinning the way only a five-year-old dog recalling puppyhood could. He was not thinking deep thoughts either.

Before realizing it, I approached the end of town. A sullen dawn reluctantly rose on the horizon, dull light smearing the tops of lathered waves. Ominous. I made the turn to head back but was only halfway home when the misting drizzle turned to serious rain and the wind kicked up a few notches. Though I wore raingear, I was getting cold, and wind-blown sand stung my face. Ouch! I picked up my pace and Gus raced the wind before me. We arrived home in record time though we jostled to see who would get through the back door first. He won.

Everyone was still sleeping when I came into the mudroom. After stretching again, I hosed and dried Gus. As a reward, he got an early breakfast and I started the coffee (and, yes, a fire) before heading upstairs to stand under a hot shower. By the time I dressed and returned to the kitchen, my mother had made her decadently rich cinnamon rolls, an Aunt Grace favorite. I set the table for breakfast in the kitchen nook, then sat with a cup of coffee and talked to Mom about things both silly and important. She always had a willing ear for both.

The rich aroma of his favorite beverage lured my father out of his bed and the cinnamon rolls seduced Grace out of hers. My mother and I brought the cinnamon rolls, coffee, and tea into the living room and within five minutes, both missing family members were downstairs.

We talked a little about the party and asked Grace to clarify a few details. Did she intend to say something to her guests? Were there specific songs she wanted played? What were her thoughts about seating arrangements? One question led to another.

Grace said she would like a little time to speak after dinner and hinted she and Antonio had been practicing something special for the event. However, like everyone else, we would need to wait and find out what she was up to. Grace's specialty was injecting the unusual into the mundane and amping up the interesting.

I left them still planning the party as I went into the kitchen to make breakfast, and quickly assembled omelets, fruit, and toast. After breakfast, Mom left to check the final party details; Dad retired to his office to do a little work; and Grace and I moseyed into the sunroom with a pot of tea to continue working the puzzle. The sounds of rain, wind, and ocean created the musical backdrop. Gus wandered in looking for a warm place to land. Of course, I built a fire for him, and he looked at me adoringly (or so I imagined) before curling up to recover from his morning workout.

Love Is in the Details

"Are you ready for today's puzzling?" Grace asked.

"I can't wait. I asked my subconscious for help before I went to sleep and I woke up excited—like a little kid on Christmas morning. Where do we start?"

Grace smiled at my eagerness as she poured herself another cup of tea and sat at the table. "Then by all means, let's begin."

As I sat opposite her, Grace motioned to the puzzle and said, "Before we begin, though, look carefully. What's the first thing you notice about the way we sorted the pieces last night?"

As directed, I examined the color piles and immediately saw what she was talking about.

"Even though we have only a little bit of natural light this morning, I can see the many color gradations within each pile. How amazing! When we initially organized the pieces under artificial light, all the colors in each pile looked relatively the same. Now I see they can be sorted more accurately."

"Good for you. You noticed the differences right away. Therefore, the *sixth* step of puzzling is to do a finer sort when you see the pieces more clearly in a different and clearer light. There's a good lesson here you can apply to your own life."

Why was I not surprised?

"Even if you've put a lot of effort into moving in a certain direction, be willing to rethink your decision when greater insight demands you re-sort the facts. I know too many people who continue to live unhappy lives because they're too proud, too stubborn, or too afraid to admit they need to change directions. They think altering their initial decision would make them look weak or wrong.

"Though your divorce from Jonathan hurt, you both called up the courage to change your minds about being together when you realized it was necessary to make a different choice. This is why you still remain friends. The decision was honest and clean and you didn't make each other wrong.

"Personally speaking, I have learned three things through a puzzle's fine-sorting process which I can apply to sorting the pieces of my life." As she spoke, I began the finer sort.

"First, I begin the process at night when I ask my subconscious to help me make clearer decisions about the initial sort I've already completed. As I *sleep on it*, I give my subconscious mind time to help. The next morning, I'm rested and able to see finer details and notice what I might have missed the day before.

"The same is true about making a decision on any important issue. Sleep on it first. Maybe sleep on it for a number of nights to let your subconscious work for you. Give the new decision time to steep in your mind and heart until you're ready to make it final. You'll know when it has brewed long enough.

"There's a reason why the saying, *seeing things in the light of day*, is common. (Another generational thing.) Light gives hope and clarity to any situation, so shine the light of your intellect; of your soul and spirit; of your enthusiasm and character onto any subject and, in time, what you want to know will become apparent.

"Secondly, if I'm miserable because I feel I'm just fumbling in the dark, I know some part of me has made the decision to be there, and this might be okay for a while. But eventually, I need to consciously shine a light on the situation and face it. It won't happen automatically and sometimes I need to remind myself to have the courage to look at things honestly.

"Finally, as you know, every job is easier when you have the proper tools. If you work on jigsaw puzzles at night, purchase a full-spectrum light to more easily see color gradations. We've already talked about first gathering everything you need before you begin a project and committing to proper planning. Then, everything will go more smoothly and you will easily improve your chances for success."

Having spoken about fine sorting, Grace explained step *seven* was essentially working the puzzle.

"Step *seven* might seem natural, but we've both known people who are great at living with great intention. They *intend* to do something and they even *plan* for it, but they never get around to truly taking action and *doing* it. Yes, the planning is important, but you must, in fact, *do* what you plan to do. Now that we've re-sorted, let's take step *seven* and get seriously started on this puzzle."

I Did It My Way

We turned our full attention to puzzling and I focused on the part I was going to work on. Taking a deep breath, I began filling in the border with the pile of matched-color puzzle pieces sitting next to it. Music was softly playing;

Grace was quietly humming; Gus was gently snoring; and rain was rhythmically beating. Peace.

I became totally lost in what I was doing and did not immediately notice Grace had approached the puzzle very differently. Instead of working around the border in front of her, she was quickly putting together pieces from a pile initially grouped next to mine. When she sensed I was watching her, she looked up and smiled.

"We certainly took two different approaches. I didn't say anything about how to begin the puzzle because there really is no right or wrong way to take step *seven*—working the puzzle. We'll be on this step for a few days, but you'll learn a lot about yourself by observing the way you approach *The Zen of Puzzles*. For example, why did you decide to work from the border?"

She waited expectantly for my answer like an excited terrier ready to pounce on a toy. Uh oh. I really reflected on my answer before replying.

"Well, I honestly didn't give it too much thought. I took the closest pile of pieces and began building up the border section directly in front of me with similar colors. How did you begin? It seems like you're much farther along than I am."

Grace did not exactly pounce, but she did seem a bit overeager to answer my question.

"I've learned once the planning is taken care of and there's no mandated process for working through a project, it doesn't really matter how I begin as long as I get the task done. If this is true, then I'll go in the direction most pleasing to me. I know this sounds deceptively simple, but I've noticed many people don't choose what truly makes them happy their starting point. Instead, they just drill down and do what they think they should do—what they've been told to do in the past.

"When I began the puzzle, I took the pile of pieces picturing the rock outcroppings—a special formation triggering many happy memories for me. I knew I would enjoy looking at and playing with the pieces, especially as they have touches of blue in the flowers, one of my favorite colors. It didn't matter to me these colors were nowhere near the part of the border in front of me. I've discovered if I first please myself when beginning a project, I can then generate much more energy and enthusiasm for whatever I'm doing.

"Because I chose a pile with my favorite things in nature with the bonus of incorporating my favorite color, I immediately became very interested in seeing how all the pieces were going to fit together. I started with the light grays and instinctively, it seemed like my hand simply gravitated to just the right piece. The process continued easily until, as you can see, I've put together a great number of pieces.

"The trick is knowing what pleases me and I started figuring this out as a child. For example, at dinner when I was told I must eat everything on my plate before having dessert, I finished the food I liked least to get it over with. This is what pleased me. Then I could enjoy the rest of the meal and look forward to something sweet.

"The same concept can be applied to puzzling. I begin working with what pleases me, either choosing my favorite colors first or my least favorite to get them behind me. I can use either approach.

"I really like to work a puzzle in sections rather than building from the border because I can focus all my attention on just the one section I'm enjoying and not worry about how the whole puzzle is going to take shape. The big picture comes later. I honor and respect each piece, each section, by focusing only on it and staying fully present to the puzzle.

"After working all the light gray pieces; finding their patterns; and putting them together, I worked the medium gray; then the dark gray; then the grays with flowers; then the blacks and browns with flowers, etc. I have no idea how they're all going to fit with each other, and I keep putting together little sections from each subgroup until transition pieces—pieces with a combination of two colors or patterns—show me how two sections can join. I love this part—when all the little groups begin to connect.

"Right now, I'm still creating my subgroups but soon, I'll discover the pattern; find the transition pieces; and maybe put one of the upper sections of the puzzle together, near the border section you've already completed. Then I'll go to the next pile and the next, eventually joining all the larger sections into the overall pattern of the puzzle.

"Why are you frowning, Rachel?"

Busted

Buying a little time, I stood and added a few logs to the fire. Gus needed to move and was not pleased.

"I'm frowning because I'm thinking. What you just explained sounds suspiciously like your philosophy of life. I suspect imbedded in your explanation are hints of how I could approach my own life differently, and I was trying to make those connections as you were speaking."

"And what did you figure out?"

"I can't believe it. I actually make things harder for myself than they need to be."

Aunt Grace looked at me with a Cheshire-cat smile. Were we going deeper into Wonderland? Alice-like, I tread carefully.

"Why do I sometimes sabotage my day the minute I wake up? Before getting out of bed, I mentally review my schedule. If the day is filled with things I like to do, I jump up, energized and looking forward to my day and remain energized until I get home. I feel centered and happy—in the zone. Nothing bothers me. But on days I think will be tedious or unbelievably busy, I drag myself out of bed and pretty much stay dragging. It's like I pre-program my responses to future events by worrying how things will turn out.

"What you said goosed my attention. If there are many right ways to approach a project, then why don't I tackle it in a way pleasing to me? Why do I so often struggle with doing it the harder way? What am I trying to prove?

"I run the pharmacy. I manage three pharmacists and five clerks over three shifts. I can set up my day and the work any way I want as long as everything gets done. However, I continue plodding along, managing the way I learned in school, from former bosses, and from past experiences. Who's to say this is now the best way to do things? Of course, I always want to be fair to my employees and not delegate all the boring jobs I don't want. But right now, I could list five or more changes potentially making work more interesting for me. I can see I've been too hesitant about delegating routine tasks I find mind-numbing. Maybe I'm actually a control freak at heart.

"I know one of the more junior pharmacists would love additional responsibility and he would be very happy to do the more routine tasks I've been holding onto for too long. Why haven't I let go? Why am I overly concerned about overwhelming him because I sometimes feel overwhelmed? Why have I not put my own happiness into the equation? Why have I been missing the obvious? Oh, good grief! I'm whining."

Of course, I accompanied this mini-outburst with a loud mournful sigh. At the same instant, Gus rolled over and sighed as well. Dog empathy.

Grace gazed thoughtfully at the fire and sipped her tea before responding.

"Because like many women, Rachel, you were raised to be the *good girl* or the *nice girl* and to put yourself second or even last. Women are told either directly or by unconscious messaging they can do it all and have it all, but nobody ever explains how this is even humanly possible.

"I'm certainly not suggesting your parents were wrong in the way they raised you. Like everybody else, you just naturally picked up behavioral messages—many of them well below your conscious awareness—from other family members, friends, schools, churches, books, song lyrics, television shows, movies, electronic games, social networks, society in general. On and on and on. The messages are endless. They constantly bombard you, telling you how you should think, look, act, and feel. If you subconsciously embrace these messages, you can easily lose yourself. You begin playing a phony role, trying to be like everyone else instead of who you truly are.

"Look at it in terms of advertising. Marketers never want you to think for yourself. They want you to believe what *they* have to say—to believe you *need* the product or service they're selling—and only then will you feel better about yourself and happier about your life. They urge you to pay attention to their ads and not to what your inner truth might be telling you. In reality, advertisers need you to put their profit goals *first* and your personal desires *second* even though they make it sound like they're totally concerned about your well-being. You've certainly lived long enough to know how deceiving these messages are.

"But it's not just advertisers. You can make the same argument for anyone or anything that fashions your *unexamined* opinions and beliefs about who you are and how you should live your life. It's critical to be vigilant and keep faith with what's true for you—to shine a light on murky messages contradicting what you know is right for you.

"Even those who think they're rebelling against the status quo ironically are often just running to the opposite side of the same spectrum, using what they're denying as the standard for what they don't want. They stay there, always thinking they're living a new and different life. However, they never create a truly original future because they're too busy looking at the past and measuring their pretend progress. They get trapped because they haven't done the inner work to learn what *they* genuinely want— what would make *them* happy.

"These pseudo-rebels play a role based on preconceived ideas about what a rebel should look and act like. They never live their own truth, just the opposite of someone else's truth. They become friends with other pseudo-rebels who think like them. Nothing new and original. Same old, same old though they think they're new and original.

"For all of these reasons, I strongly believe you need to put yourself at the top of your priority list. If you don't first take care of yourself and make yourself happy, then how can you possibly take care of anybody else? I'm going to let you think about this point for a few minutes while I go into the kitchen for more hot water."

Grace took the teapot and left, and I walked to the window to watch the storm. High tide had arrived and I could already see there would be beach erosion. What a wild ride both the beach and I were having. I wondered what old ideas about myself would erode by the end of this process. Already it was starting.

What is my truth? What really pleased me? Was I living by someone else's standards? We were just beginning to work the puzzle, but my thoughts churned as madly as the ocean. High tide had arrived inside as well.

Grace walked in and smiled knowingly, guessing what her comments had triggered. I returned to the table as she continued the conversation.

"We were talking about taking care of yourself first. You've probably heard this example before, but I think it's still one of the best to illustrate this point. If you're traveling by plane and there's a quick loss of cabin pressure, you're directed to put on your own oxygen mask first before helping others put theirs on. If you pass out due to lack of oxygen, you certainly won't be able to assist others.

"This is good advice for everything. Take care of yourself before you try to help those you care about, and all else will naturally follow. This is not selfish. Honoring yourself first means acknowledging your value and worth. It means using your self-respect and self-love to define your personal boundaries. It means tending to the most important relationship you will ever have—the relationship of you with you.

"The golden rule states, *do unto others as you would have them do unto you*, but let's think about this a little more. Like the old programming axiom, *garbage in, garbage out,* the end result of doing unto others is directly related to how you first do unto yourself.

"When you unlovingly feed yourself a constant stream of doubt and negative self-talk—garbage in—you end up accepting the hurtful behavior of others—garbage out. You might even retaliate and try to hurt them back—more garbage out. And, even if you think you're treating someone well, if you are motivated by duty and obligation rather than by sincere caring, this is garbage out as well—no matter how nice the garbage smells.

"Always first treat yourself well, Rachel. Only then can you treat others the way you, in turn, would like to be treated. When self-love finally leads, it's amazing how those who have tried to give you a hard time begin to naturally disappear from your life. It's just the way it works. Lead from love. Begin with yourself. Move beyond the *shoulds* of duty and obligation drilled into you since you were very young. Operate from your love.

"Going a step further, if you're living a decent loving life, then your only valid directive becomes, *do what you want with harm to none*. Nothing else makes sense.

"We go to extremes in this culture. We're encouraged either to think only of ourselves to satisfy the demands of others, or we're pushed in the opposite direction to total self-sacrifice. If you notice, the message about self-sacrifice frequently comes from those who want to control you for their own personal, economic, or political purposes.

"Remember *doing harm to none* also means doing no harm *to yourself*. Many forget this and sacrifice their own emotional needs to satisfy others. Therefore, practice *Divine Selfishness,* honoring the sanctity of all life because you first honor your own. Let go of any cookie-cutter, subtly imposed ways of living and become your own unique person.

"This might be more difficult for those born into cultures founded on putting the desires of family first, so they have more to work though. But you don't have this extra layer of messaging, and be grateful you don't need to sort through those particular *shoulds*.

"Again, I'm not advocating negative-ego-driven selfishness or self-indulgence, but having a sacred pact with yourself and the Divine within and honoring the relationship. Act with Divine Selfishness and all good things will result over time. I promise."

Chapter Six

Keeping Faith

Returning her attention to the puzzle, Grace was quiet and gave me time to ponder what she just said. She had never been as forthcoming with me—not like this. She had always simply been my Aunt Grace, honest and funny, supportive and kind, but she was not in the habit of revealing her deepest thoughts and feelings about how she lived her life. I sensed she was passing on her life's legacy to me in the only way she knew how. I was deeply moved.

I watched her for a while, noticing how she worked the pieces—holding them lightly, studying them, admiring them, moving them around to sense all their possibilities. She honored them. She was intimate with each piece, and I realized this was how she approached everything and everyone in her life. Did puzzling teach her how to be fully engaged and present? Or did she learn to do puzzling because of the way she lived her life? Which was the chicken? Which, the egg?

Looking at how I handled things, I knew I was great with the holding, studying, examining, and moving-around parts—the parts involving mental focus and discipline. However, the taking-time-to-admire part; the honoring-each-small-piece part; and the being-present part were more elusive. In scope, these were the-way-of-the-heart parts—the parts that could never be controlled—the parts I regularly denied.

Do what you want with harm to none. Could I really live this way? If I had been responsible for my own happiness and truly accepted and honored how Jonathan was trying to find his own happiness, would we still be together? If I knew in every cell of my body I was currently living life in a way bringing profound happiness, could I truly minimize what partner, parents, family, friends, acquaintances, and co-workers thought of the *form* my happiness took? Did I have enough courage to be who I was truly meant to be? I always thought of myself as a strong person, but was I courageous? I knew Grace certainly was.

She lived her life with flat-out devotion to what pleased her and what brought her joy while zestily suffusing everything with love, even if the form it took made no sense to anyone except her. In the process, she pleased many, but certainly not all. Some in her circle did not like Grace—even despised her—but she remained true to who she was. Could I do the same?

I tucked all these thoughts away in a mental file labeled *things to think about while running*, and got back to the puzzle. I stopped working it the way I had begun—the one-by-one-by-one method appearing very logical at the time—and began examining all the puzzle piles for the colors pleasing me most. The bright reds caught my eye, and I pulled them to where I was sitting. I noticed how I was able to place the pieces much more quickly since I was working with colors I enjoyed.

We puzzled for another hour in silence; each wrapped in our own thoughts; focusing on our own puzzle section. I pretty much completed the reds—poppies blowing on the sloping crest of a small hill. The photo on the box illustrated the reds waterfalling into a mix of yellows and oranges before spilling into a spring-green meadow of mostly yellow flowers. This river of color eventually narrowed into a stream of blues. I knew I would enjoy working on the rest of the flowers, and I pulled them toward me and began playing.

Grace completed a section of rock outcroppings near the bottom border before switching to the blues of sky. She was just working through a light-blue pile when she glanced up saying, "I noticed some of these blue pieces for the sky are transition pieces because they include the red poppies as well. Would you like to see if we can join our sections together?"

I was up for the challenge and consequently connected the two sections. We first kept turning them to see where the shapes lined up. After a few misses, we were able to join the two sections, and the outlines of three missing pieces became obvious. Since we knew their exact shapes, I quickly located the one elusive missing red and Grace discovered her two blues.

Sky and poppies bloomed before us. The joining was a fast and painless process, and we were both hugely satisfied at seeing the sections come together and the larger pattern emerge.

Look Both Ways before Crossing

I asked her to tell me a little more about transition pieces. Grace explained these were the puzzle pieces sending her in a new direction and suggesting links to other puzzle sections. Transition pieces could be a combination of two distinct colors and patterns, or be totally surprising and unexpected. Grace thought they were the most important pieces of the puzzle. Until she found them, she focused on a single color or pattern while trusting she would eventually come across the transition pieces to connect the section to the whole. These transition pieces were the fulcrum points shifting everything, and Grace had borrowed the transition concept from her own life.

Going to New York when she was only sixteen was the transition piece connecting her childhood and adult worlds. The move to Las Vegas was the transition piece joining her modeling and dancing work, leading to her independence. Having the forgotten weekend linked her going-with-the-flow part of life with a more self-examined phase, eventually bringing her financial freedom. Becoming a croupier transitioned her to Harold. Doing foundation work in Harold's name transitioned her to George.

Grace described transitions as triggers brought about by the choices we make, connecting very different phases of our lives. We could use these transitions either to develop a broader perspective about beginning a new chapter of our current lives or moving in an entirely different direction.

This conversation bridged easily to another topic Aunt Grace wanted to discuss.

"You asked a question yesterday about you and Jonathan—about whether you would still be together if you had encouraged him to always do what he wanted to do. You said you ask yourself this question a lot. To help you answer it for yourself, tell me what you felt when you were putting these two sections together."

I stared at her. "The puzzle again? Really? Okay, here goes.

"I felt excited when I saw the bigger, overall pattern begin to emerge as the puzzle sections came together. I enjoyed doing my section of reds, but I was also interested in seeing how the reds were going to fit into the whole. I didn't feel any sense of competition with you. I trusted you were having a good time putting your rock and blue pieces in place, and when we were working together, I honestly experienced just curiosity and appreciation.

"When the two sections did come together, I felt a growing sense of satisfaction. The shape of the three missing pieces was clearly evident and it made locating them very easy. It was a true cooperative effort, and the timing of joining the sections worked for me because we each had the opportunity to make progress on our own part. Is this what you were asking?"

"Precisely. Now to make parallels to some of the things we talked about earlier, note our partnership never became competitive because we were working on what we each enjoyed. You trusted I was doing my best to complete the blue section, and I trusted you were working diligently on the red. There are hints here for good relationships.

"When you are happy with what you're doing and know your partner is happy in what he's doing, you both can bring more to the relationship because it's firmly established on trust. When you and Jonathan joined your lives together, what you both needed to work on became more evident. If you expect and accept this *missing-pieces* condition as something normal and natural, you can then work together on locating those pieces, filling in the blanks, and jointly building your life. After taking this step, a bigger pattern will begin to emerge you can both agree on and enjoy.

"As you would suspect, timing is a very big factor in a relationship. It's important to know when your partner is willing to take a step. I'd asked if you were ready to merge your section with mine before I suggested we proceed. If you wanted to work on your section for a bit longer, I would have been fine and just continued focusing on the medium-blue pieces and thoroughly enjoyed working on the section. If I rushed you, we would not have arrived at the same comfortable place. Are you with me so far?"

"Yes. I think it's brilliant and makes a lot of sense. Thanks. The transition concept can help me figure out what went sideways with Jonathan and me. Now you've made me even more curious about what will come up when we join the next sections!"

Negotiation

"Speaking about sections," said Grace," I'm going to redirect my focus from the blues to yet another color. I'm thinking about working on the orange-and-yellow flowers. Is my direction okay with you? And answer me honestly. Don't be nice or polite."

I laughed, "Well, about an hour ago, I would have told you it would be fine with me if you switched to the oranges and yellows, but it's also where I was going to go next. Okay, wise one, how do we handle this?"

"Let's talk about it a little. When I look at the photo on the puzzle box, I see a broad section of the hill where the oranges and yellows are mixed; another almost entirely filled with yellow flowers; and then the stream area bordered by mostly blue flowers. There are rock outcroppings with both blue and yellow flowers on three sides. Should we divide the puzzle this way and each take what we would most enjoy working on? We can swap pieces if we find we have a few the other needs."

"Sounds reasonable to me. Let's try it and see how it goes. And I know your next question will be about my preference. I would like to continue moving down the hill from the red flowers and work on the mixed yellow-and orange flowers. Okay with you?"

Grace paused a beat to think about it and then said, "I would have enjoyed working on them, but it's not my greatest preference. I really want to work on the flowers beside the stream. Those colors would please me most and I can connect them to the rock section I've already completed. However, if I greatly wanted to work on your orange-and-yellow flowers, what would you have said?"

"Gosh. What a good question. What *would* I have said?" I asked as I stared out the window where blankets of rain obscured the ocean. I thought about how I handled these kinds of situations with Jonathan.

"Yesterday, I would have just let you work on the yellow-and-orange flowers and probably mentally griped about it, but today, I honestly would have spoken up and somehow resolved it with you. Maybe we would have worked on them together, or maybe we would each have worked on something else entirely and saved the section to the end.

"When thinking about how this type of situation played out with Jonathan, you're right—I mostly went with the flow and pretty much did what he wanted to do. But Jonathan knew what I enjoyed, and he was very good at finding things for us to do where we would both have a good time. I never felt like it was all about him.

"Truthfully, though, if it ever came to a showdown about doing something he wanted to do versus what I wanted to do, I would usually give in. I held onto the confused belief that being a good partner meant conceding—the willingness to be the one who always gives in. Looking at it now, the notion seems a bit pathetic and pathological."

Grace chuckled and shook her head. "I don't know if I'd go as far, but a true partnership is really like the tidal ebb and flow of the invisible ocean you're trying very hard to see. There must be a graceful and gracious give and take, but if you're the one always doing the giving, then your tide will go out so far, no one will be able to reach you."

Startled, I looked back at her before responding. "But let me clarify something. I don't want you to think I was always the one doing the giving. Jonathan is a wonderful man and, in so many ways, he was also a wonderful husband. It's just we were both so damned politically correct, so damned *nice*, and so caught up in our separate careers—both of us—I now wonder whether we were always as honest as we needed to be to keep the relationship healthy and alive. Working things through can take a lot of effort.

"We never gave each other enough time and attention—enough true intimacy. Sometimes I wondered whether we were following a learned playbook about what a great couple should look like, dictating how we ought to act.

"I would say 'Yes' to things I hated doing because I knew he would enjoy them. But, looking back, I never did them with great joy or enthusiasm and he knew it. I was politely interested, but resignation is no way to be with a partner, and Jonathan was the same way with me. I always knew when he was into something I really wanted to do or when he was just putting on a good front.

"We never talked about it later, I guess because we were both trying hard to *say* the right thing and *do* the right thing. Bottom line? We were just not as honest with each other as we needed to be, maybe because we were both not honest with ourselves. I can see things more clearly now. But how did *you* handle it when your partners wanted to do something you hated?"

See You Later, Honey

Grace smiled as if recalling fond memories and said, "I let them do it with my blessing and they would go without me. If I could not be 100% enthusiastic in my participation in something, I would not be part of the event. I always gave Harold and George the freedom to do what they wanted, either by themselves or with their friends, without making them feel the least bit guilty. They gave the same freedom to me. We each found this to be a much more interesting and honest way to live.

"If there were things I was mildly interested in, my partners always asked if I wanted to go, and I often joined them. The *asking* is the important part. I first thought about what would please me and also considered what would please them. If I didn't want to go and the event wasn't particularly important to my partners, they went without me, but they always asked. Using these guidelines, when we frequently did things together, we thoroughly enjoyed both the experiences and being with each other.

"In each relationship, the two individuals usually have similar interests they can appreciate together, but they also might have diverse interests, unfamiliar to their partner. For me, I decided to learn more about what appealed to my partners because I wanted to be with them and I liked exploring new subjects and ideas. However, I never did anything because I felt I *should*.

"For example, Harold loved art, and though the subject was at first not one of my top interests, he taught me about the different forms and periods of art. As a result, I came to appreciate art and liked going with him to art events and discussing them later. George did not like opera when we first got together, but he attended a few productions with me and got hooked.

"As we grew and changed as individuals, we grew and changed as a couple. Being open to what interested the other added to the richness of the relationship. Part of tending a relationship, though, is being sure there's a balance between doing things solo and doing things together. Paying attention to this balance is critical if you don't want to end up living separate lives. Understand your motivations and be honest with yourself and your partner. Honesty is fundamental to building trust in each other.

"Share what you can with all your heart and let your partner enjoy his own interests. Now, let me explain an exception to this rule.

"Being a victim or martyr in a relationship is not healthy and should never be part of the partnership formula. However, there were many times when I chose out of love to do something I knew would not particularly please me simply because my partner wanted to experience the event *with me* and would take great pleasure in my accompanying him. To an outsider, it might have looked like I gave in but in reality, I pleased myself first, but in a different way.

"I chose to go to his special event because I truly enjoyed watching how happy it made him to be with me for a shared experience. From my perspective, it was another way to express my love. We both, then, got what we wanted without self-sacrifice of any kind. Therefore, you can add willingness and love to the relationship mix of trust and honesty.

"When children are involved, this gets much more complicated because you need to work out with your partner how to accommodate the needs of the children. I've witnessed real issues when a conscious choice for children was not made by both partners. For these couples, parenting became a burden, and one of the partners usually ended up resenting what he or she (and other parenting combinations), perceived as the unequal division of child-raising responsibilities. If you marry again and decide to have children, be sure you both make a *conscious choice* for children and parenting. Parenting, even with its sometimes drudgery, can be a sacred act when undertaken in love."

Both Gus and I looked up at the same time when she made this last statement. I looked at Aunt Grace and Gus looked at me, perhaps envisioning future shrieking children invading his peaceful home.

"Stop. Please explain your last point a little more."

"Think about it. Children bring huge responsibilities. Having children by default because it's the expected thing to do or, God forbid, save your marriage, is ultimately cruel. If you default into either of these two conditions, parenting will eventually undermine the relationship with your partner, and the children will greatly suffer as a result.

"I've heard women—and it's usually women—say they're always sacrificing for their families to ensure everyone is happy and cared for, even if it means the woman ends up doing things she hates. Now think about this. It's understandable most parents get tired of constantly washing clothes; driving to an untold number of kid events; or shopping for food—all while holding a job—but all these tasks are a part of managing a household and children.

"Every kind of work, no matter how glamorous it appears, has its own tedious or boring tasks. You've already mentioned some of yours. However, if those tasks are performed with care and attention and with an appreciation for how they fit into the larger picture, they can become genuine expressions of love.

"With care and attention, you can pack school lunches or get children ready for bed because these tasks are all part of the larger picture called parenting. Boring routine can be seen as a natural part of tending the parent-child relationship. I know when you're dead tired, it's hard to reach for loftier sentiments, but practice can get you there. However, this is important. Always keep in mind *sacrifice* should never enter the picture unless it is understood in its original meaning of *making sacred or holy*.

"I repeat—unless a woman is taking care of herself first, she cannot truly care for others, even in the name of love. Only victims and martyrs follow formulaic ways of acting they learned from someone else. If these unaware women who sacrifice themselves at the altar of duty and obligation don't start out as victims or martyrs, they could easily end up as either.

"Real love means loving yourself enough to create the capacity to extend your love to others. I cannot say this too often—love is not about duty and obligation. Love is about gifting another from a full and free heart. I see you frowning. What are you thinking about now?"

Reruns

"While you were talking," I said, "a number of scenes involving Jonathan and me flashed through my mind. I realize now I was totally unaware of being caught up in a formulaic life and I think the same was true for him. Honestly, I wonder if we really knew each other even after all the years we'd spent together.

"Then I thought about several of my friends who seem to be headed in the same direction. The ones who are just *grinning and bearing it*, saying they feel cut off from their partners but they continue to just drift along. I wonder if becoming a victim or martyr in the name of love and living a formulaic life have something to do with their unhappiness."

Grace replied, "You have a point. It's why first marriages or first profound relationships can serve us if we let them because they teach us so much about everything we're talking about. Primarily, they offer greater clarity by providing insights about what's really important to us in relationships. Of course, this is different for everyone. I'm referencing the ideal here.

"I know I was much better to George because I first had the deep relationship with Harold who helped me understand and handle many of my don't-trust-men issues. Harold and I went through rocky patches because we were both trying to figure out how to be more honest with each other at a time when we were surrounded by formulaic people who never ceased to be both taken aback and offended by the freedom we gave each other. But we decided to follow our own interests and have our own circle of friends. Working through these issues brought us closer together."

She paused and was silent, waiting for me to voice the question she saw in my eyes. I stared at her briefly before lowering my eyes and asking in a wobbly voice, "Then why, Aunt Grace, couldn't Jonathan and I have worked through our issues and stayed together like you and Harold did?" Grace saw my pain and reached over to take my hand.

"First of all, don't go there. Don't ever compare yourself or your relationship to any other. It's a trap. As every person is unique and distinct, each relationship will be unrepeatable and different as well. Secondly, don't beat yourself up for an event from your past, even your most recent past. Can you honestly say you got up each morning and did the best you could?"

"Yes, but some days I know I tried harder than others."

"Good. Then you're still part of the human race. Up-and-down days are perfectly normal. But if you set out to do your best each day, you cannot look back now with regret.

"When you were fifteen-years-old, it would have been silly to look back at your two-year-old self and call her *stupid* because she couldn't write or tie her own shoes. At thirty, you didn't judge your younger 13-year-old as *inept* because she couldn't drive or didn't know how to pair wines with meals. You get my point. Love yourself enough to have compassion for who you were then, who you are today, and who you are becoming. This is vitally important.

"Now, in this very moment—having gained wisdom and a broader perspective about relationships—you can reflect on your years with Jonathan and, of course, you will see areas where you were not as skilled and strong as you are today, even a few months later. Let all your emerging insights be okay. Don't beat yourself up. Have compassion for your younger self; learn from her; and be grateful for the learning. Then thank your younger self who tried very, very hard and was filled with such incredible pain. Bless her, and move on."

By the time she finished speaking, my tears were silently flowing. Grace quietly got up and came to me, held me, rocked me gently, and then let me go when I finally calmed down. As I wiped away my tears, I looked at her, expecting she would say something comforting and profound.

"Isn't growth fun?" she asked a bit too enthusiastically as I rolled my swollen eyes.

"It's time for a break," we said together and laughed.

"Great minds!" I said.

"And connected hearts," Grace responded. Of course, I wholeheartedly gave her statement two thumbs up.

Not having thumbs, Gus loudly barked in agreement.

Chapter Seven

The Gnarly Side of Puzzling

We both took some time to answer phone messages. When I came downstairs, I found Grace bundled up on the front veranda, sipping tea with my mother. There was a rare break in the storm and they had found a warm spot on the swing where a peek-a-boo sun could find them. Gus snoozed under the swing, legs kicking as he doggy-dreamed.

I noticed how the light picked up the gold threads in the purple-and-blue jacket Grace was wearing, and I thought how stunning she looked—like an empress holding court with her lady-in-waiting. Things stood still. Grace became timeless. I felt privileged she was a part of my family and grateful she held such a central place in my life.

I let them have their privacy and poured my own cup of tea before going upstairs to the porch above them. I sat in a silvered-out rocking chair and invited the in-and-out sun to come play with me as well. My brain (and heart) had been working hard and I let both rest, trusting my subconscious was doing its part to put all this information into patterns I could use later.

I closed my eyes and listened to the wind teasing the leaves, daring the last ones to fall. The waves still crashed, but their sucking retreat across the sand was a muted shushing accompanying my slow back-and-forth movement. I smiled at Mom's and Grace's frequent laughter. I felt fully at peace with my world.

Think Again

My world? Was this *my* world—a childhood world that brought such belonging and security? Was I trying to recreate what my parents had built—a world I unconsciously inherited from them? Had I *really* engineered a world unique to me, one reflecting my true preferences, or was I settling for a copycat world, no matter how pleasant it might be?

Good grief! Where did those questions come from? And why were they coming up now? I relegated them to my handy thoughts-while-running file because I simply did not want to think about anything possibly disturbing my stillpoint moment. I was too much at peace to deal with deeper issues. And then it happened.

A little-used part of me shouted for my immediate attention. It grabbed me and wouldn't let me go, filling me with mounting urgency. With it came an escalating tension, rising and intensifying, fuller and stronger, and when it finally exploded, suffused every part of me with a new understanding, leaving me wondering and breathless. Then and there, I actually experienced one—no, not an orgasm—but a huge crazy *aha moment* like Grace had promised. Between one breath and the next, the way I knew myself to be within my overly-controlled-and-thought-out world came apart and rearranged itself. Just like that.

After the first wave of awareness passed and I confirmed I was still myself, I was filled with a driving energy, calling for immediate action. I opened my eyes; walked to the end of the balcony; and with the vast ocean as a silent witness, I spoke aloud a willed and heartfelt promise to both myself and to my world. I pledged there would be no more sacrificing! No more putting myself second! No more drama! I would be *Reactive Rachel* no longer!

In a suspended moment, the conscious part of me chose another way, a truer and more authentic way. I stood tall and strong, confident in my knowing that all the many aspects of who I was would eventually align with my choice. From this time on, I'd make more conscious decisions. I'd become a better version of myself. I'd put on my superhero's cape and become *Responsive Rachel*, the one who remained fully present; the one who listened before taking action; the one whose heart was more open and accepting. I *would* be different.

Following this bold declaration, all I could think was, "Well, that was certainly an interesting ride."

Before my very human, are-you-crazy voice hustled in to label this *aha moment* as just another experience, I wanted to look at it through the eyes of my greater, eternal self. I returned to rocking quietly, taking the time to play with the pieces of my clearer-eyed knowing—becoming familiar with this just-discovered part of me.

I must have dozed off soon after my declaration because when I woke up, my tea was cold and the wind was sending newly arrived rain in my direction. I suddenly realized I was hungry. Apparently, the first order of business was to see about lunch.

I found Dad downstairs in the kitchen, obviously having the same thought. He possessively clutched the remains of the second loaf of bread I had made the previous evening and stood intently in front of the refrigerator, as if awaiting divine direction about what to pile on his holy sandwich.

I smiled at his intensity and said, "Mom baked a ham yesterday afternoon for sandwiches and I thought I would make lunch. Would you like me to use your bread when I make yours? I'll be using rye bread for everyone else." Thanking me and happily relinquishing his almost-whole loaf, Dad took his coffee to the living room to learn what my mother and Aunt Grace had been plotting in his absence.

After a while, Mom arrived to set the table in the kitchen nook overlooking the back garden where the wind was trying its best to decapitate the last of the heartier flowers, lurching drunkenly back and forth. I was deeply grateful for this suspended time-out-of-time. Little by little, I seemed to be falling in love with life all over again. From working a puzzle? Who knew?

The minute I announced, "Lunch is ready!" the family trooped in led by my father who immediately claimed his sandwich. My mother eyed him balefully but didn't say a word as he proceeded to complete his gastronomic masterpiece with even more ham, cheese, and mustard. It's a good thing he stays active.

Somehow, we got on the subject of favorite jokes and essentially spent lunch laughing and eating. We skipped dessert since we decided to go out to dinner at one of the local restaurants offering wonderful seafood specials on Tuesday nights. There is nothing like good food to stimulate thoughts of more good food.

After lunch, Mom and Grace cleaned up and Dad went upstairs to continue working as Gus trailed behind. I returned to the puzzle.

Returning to the Scene of the Action

I focused on the section of orange-and-yellow flowers, but the pieces were much more complicated than the reds. With the red flowers, I'd used the top of the hill as a reference, but the oranges and yellows were all jumbled together and looked almost the same. To make things easier, I divided the large pile by flower pattern into five smaller groups. At first, the patterns weren't very obvious, but the more I played with the pieces, the more I noticed distinctions and the easier they were to place. Of course, now that my brain was switched on and making comparisons between puzzling and my life, I wondered how

I could apply this particular puzzle lesson. The music of understanding began to blast.

I realized I took risks only if they came neatly wrapped in familiar reference points and kept me safely in my comfort zone. Becoming a pharmacist had not really been a big risk because I was already familiar with the work before I went to university. In high school, my pharmacist uncle had hired me for the summer and later, I interned with him. Therefore, no big deal.

Marrying Jonathan was not risky because we had known each other for almost five years before we were married, and everyone important in my life liked and accepted him. After my divorce, I bought a house in a nice neighborhood with the security that friends lived nearby.

Had I ever taken a real risk without a safe and familiar reference point? What would happen if I did? Grace left her Indiana home and moved to New York without a clue about what she was going to do, and then she moved sight-unseen to Las Vegas. What real risks—those without reference points—had I taken?

However, I did not believe taking real risks meant being foolish. Grace had arranged a guaranteed place to stay before she traveled to New York. She did not simply arrive hoping for the best. She went to Las Vegas with someone she knew. She became certain about Harold before moving to New York with him.

Grace had simply stepped into the stream of her life and allowed the flow to take her to new places. One step led to another because she was open to change and willing to do what was needed to grow. She also knew how to survive.

It was sobering to realize I had arrived at this time of my life without having taken a *real* risk and, in my heart, I recognized I still lacked courage. A part of me was willing to opt for security rather than for exploration. A part was content to stay in the comfortable and familiar and deny growth and change—to settle for a safe little life. Now that this alarming fact had unexpectedly shown up, I knew I had to make decisions differently. I needed to stop making choices guaranteeing sameness. Right! That's what I would do from now on. Guaranteed.

Really?

Would I be courageous enough? Though I was now cautiously gung-ho, I had no clue about what this might mean and lead to. I just knew it was important. My life—MY life—literally depended on it. Yes! Let's get to it.

Furthermore, when I looked at how much time I'd taken to carefully separate all the orange-and-yellow pieces, it hit me how often I did not give the same level of attention to noticing and appreciating the finer gradations in the people around me. Initially, I thought the pieces in the puzzle piles were similar in color and I could have dismissed their almost-sameness if I had not looked carefully at each one, touched it, admired it, and connected with it.

How many opportunities did I miss to know good and interesting people—people who could make my life fuller and far better—because I looked at them too quickly or simply shuffled them into preconceived cat-egories? How often did I segregate these people into standard groups using outdated reference points coming not from my inner truth, but from outside messages? How frequently did I take the time to meet others with an open heart—without arbitrary filters—and see them for the individuals they were?

The puzzle was certainly speaking to me and I was obviously listening. This must be at the heart of the *Zen of Puzzles*—the listening for discovery; the play of learning; the permitting of new knowing; the *Zen* Grace talked about.

Before I could forget these ideas, I ran upstairs and recorded both the insights from this morning's puzzling session and those just popping up. By the time I returned to the sunroom, Grace was at the puzzle working on the blue flowers by the stream.

"I see you've sorted the piles for the next colors. Did any new ideas come up for you?" she asked. Perhaps the silly grin gave me away.

I gave her a thumbnail summary of what I had written expressing again my surprise at how much I was learning through conscious puzzling. She listened until I ran out of words, and then with great kindness, Grace explained courage did not mean I would never be afraid. Courage meant I would feel fear—perhaps even terror—but take action despite my feelings because it was the right thing to do. She reminded me that taking the action to divorce Jonathan had been a courageous step. With all my heart, I wanted to believe her.

Grace thought those who never knew fear were either unconscious or reckless. Then she switched topics.

Isn't That Interesting?

"Did you know there are people who play golf and use it as a spiritual practice? I wasn't aware of this until Antonio told me that sometimes Japanese golfers use the game to measure how internally centered and aligned they are. After talking to his two friends, they tried it. They noticed if they're in the flow, their drives are straight and long, and their putting is unerring and decisive. When they're off-center and out of the flow, their golfing game is messy. It made a lot of sense to me, and I decided to use puzzling to gauge how I'm doing with staying in the flow.

"I figured out that when I'm working the puzzle and getting frustrated and impatient, my feelings are telling me inner messages are waiting to be delivered, and I better pay attention. If everything flows well and the puzzle comes together with ease, then I know I'm in my flow. I use puzzling to determine exactly how centered I am; to find what I need to do to return to center; and to help me practice staying in the flow."

I stopped her. "What do you mean by the *flow*? I know what I mean by it, but I'd love to hear your definition."

"The simplest way I can explain being in the flow is living in a centered state where everything around me lines up naturally, so I'm able to move through each part of my day with ease and grace. No pun intended.

For example, when I'm out of the flow, I often spill tea or accidentally break things; I realize I've forgotten an important paper when I'm halfway to a meeting; I choose the wrong line at the grocery store and wait forever. I could go on and on, but I'm sure you have your own examples. Essentially, I'm distracted.

"On the other hand, when I'm *in* the flow, I find a parking spot right away; connect immediately on the phone with just the right person; quickly find what I need to buy when I shop. Again, I could continue, but you get the point.

"When I'm centered and feeling good about myself and positive and hopeful about life, I seem to flow with everything and everyone around me instead of knocking into them, causing them to knock back. Puzzling is a way for me to slow down and return to center. Taking time to engage in a fun and relaxing activity is a sure way of maintaining my balance and staying in the flow."

I stopped her again.

"Okay. Let me get this straight. You're saying the more I can stay connected through my heart to everything and everyone around me by staying centered and aware, then the easier life will be because I can remain in the natural flow of things. Right?"

"Yes, that's a great summary, Rachel. I do believe you're on your way to becoming quite proficient in grasping the *Zen of Puzzles*."

A smile was my response. Time would tell.

Even though It Quacks like a Duck

"I have another question. At times you say *working* the puzzle and at other times, you say *playing* with the puzzle. Is there a difference? Are the terms interchangeable? What do you mean by each?"

Grace paused to consider my questions. I loved how precise she always tried to be with her answers.

"I was just reflecting on when work and play become almost synonymous to me. I think it was around the time I turned fifty. I looked upon my fiftieth birthday as the midpoint of my life and really thought about what I wanted to do with the second half. Therefore, after that birthday, I took a halftime break and spent two weeks by myself in the mountains to figure it out.

"By then, I had worked very hard to achieve certain goals. I thought this was all well and good and was appropriate for how I'd lived the first half of my life. However, I wanted to reframe what work really meant to me, what life could really hold for me. I spent days coming up with definitions speaking as much to my heart as my head. After pondering the question and connecting with my subconscious mind, I created a new definition of work, one aligning more truly with the woman I'd become.

"Work, for me, became an opportunity to engage with talented individuals in interesting and challenging activities, allowing me to play with life and people to achieve certain ends. In turn, this play-through-work would bring greater understanding and compassion for myself and those I loved; for those I worked with; and for the world around me.

"I knew that like the puzzle process, difficult issues would arise, but I could change them into riddles to solve and, in turn, they would lead to better solutions for everyone. If you look at my play-through-work definition carefully, you can see I essentially reframed my life as one big puzzle I could work with and fully enjoy.

"No more slogging through things. No more struggling and wrestling with situations depleting my energy. I was able to move from operating only as a *warrior*—knocking down barriers; scaling mountains; fighting the good fight—to living as an *adventurer*—approaching thorny situations with curiosity; sourcing new ways to handle recurring issues more creatively; opening my heart wider and putting myself into the shoes of others so kindness became a bigger part of the mix. Over time, I turned the complexities of work into the play of puzzling.

"Don't get me wrong. There is room for both these aspects of self, and I still call upon the warrior in me when needed, but I summon her less and less and only in the toughest situations. It takes a lot of practice to know when to use both sets of skills."

"Like learning to fight for a Manhattan cab at rush hour?" I asked. We both laughed.

"But I honestly don't have a lot of taxi issues anymore. The warrior comes out when I face impasses, like handling fractious bullies at contract negotiations. It's fascinating to see how people try to dominate a situation thinking this is the way they need to act to get what they want. This is another reason why it's good to have boundaries.

"Usually, though, because I enjoy being the adventurer, I tend to attract people and situations allowing me to naturally function through this aspect. However, I still call on the fierce protective warrior to head off those who try to abuse the people I love and what I care about. It's important to be both a warrior and an adventurer, but be clear about when you're going to invite each to handle a situation.

"Become more aware when each personality aspect is on center stage. Living on autopilot is living unconsciously. You end up as a minor character in your life's story while other characters step in to write your script."

I just kept nodding as Grace made each point, hoping it made me look wise.

"Did I change immediately and practice my newfound philosophy impeccably? Of course not. Changing lanes in life takes skill, and I intentionally used the word *practice* when I talked about my change. Significantly altering a long-held perspective is a learned skill, and I was continuously mindful about which operating style I was using. I would first pause when faced with a major decision and switched to a different aspect when needed. Afterwards, I would be absolutely honest with myself about my progress or lack of progress. Not wanting to fool myself kept me on track.

"This shift to an adventurer perspective eventually became my *usual* perspective. However, as I've mentioned, when I'm under stress or when I require them, I still reach for tried-and-true warrior skills to break through obstacles.

"I'm also much better at noticing when my warrior shows up when she's not really needed. I can more quickly send her away before I go on a mental rampage and spill too much blood—my own or that of others. But under stress, the knee-jerk reaction to call up my warrior is always there, and I need to be constantly vigilant. You'll need to have lots and lots of practice as well, but you're beginning a whole lot earlier than I did.

"I never would have put this into words unless you'd asked me. Thank you, Rachel." I preened a bit before she continued.

"To summarize. Instead of *doing work*, I began seeing everything as *play* by taking things less seriously and lightening up. Some of this mental refocusing was easy and some of it, challenging. I had to keep reminding myself, though, I would always be dealing with both types of experiences which ultimately make life—whether I called it work or play—amazing and fascinating. Things certainly became much more meaningful. I believe you'll find this out for yourself when you keep practicing."

Grace must have noticed my now-glazed eyes and far-away stare.

"Rachel, are you with me? You look like you're not really here."

I snapped back to the present. "I guess I was only half listening. Sorry. I was just thinking about how you impressed me when I was a little girl. Your presence filled a room and you were always warm and funny. Even as a child, I knew you were someone special. But you also seemed to be more serious and even a little distant.

"When I got older, you seemed to become more approachable. I thought maybe it was just my growing up and understanding you better, but never never guessed you changed because you chose to become different. Whoa! I guess I need to wrap my mind around this revelation a little more and might have more questions for you after I take some time to think about what you've just said."

"We can all change, Rachel, if we know what's important and do the necessary inner work to focus our energies differently." She underscored this last message by pouring tea for both of us.

"I began to practice reframing my life and before long, I felt as if I were looking at everything with new eyes. I became more curious about people and things in a way I hadn't felt since childhood. I allowed myself to explore opportunities I would have ignored before. I had more adventures. I let in more love.

"Work became play in the sense I was playing my life as a musician plays a fine instrument. Who I am in my totality is the only instrument I have while I'm here on Earth. I was determined to become a virtuoso at playing this instrument and fully expressing my life. I feel like I've succeeded in achieving a degree of mastery, but there is still always more to learn as the world changes and the people in my life keep growing and changing as well.

"For me, work and play are now interchangeable if

I'm engaged in an activity I enjoy, or if I'm with people who encourage me to play the instrument of who-I-am in a way pleasing to me. Only then do I have anything worthwhile to share with others. Maybe this sounds idealistic and initially, it was also very aspirational. However, over the years and after a lot of practice, this became my standard for interacting with the world, and I thoroughly delight in it. Did I fill in some of the blanks for you?"

"Yes, completely. Thank you. I'll certainly think about what you've said. Good stuff, Aunt Grace."

We worked for another hour before Grace decided to go upstairs and rest before dinner. I intended to keep working/playing for a little longer. Before she left, Grace commented, "Remember you're working the puzzle to integrate information or experience your own pleasure. Puzzling can balance your body, mind, and spirit, but you must be careful not to tax your body too much and push it out of balance.

"Puzzles can pull you and when they do, you might completely lose track of time. You need to stay attuned to your body and its needs. Take breaks. Eat at your usual times. Stretch. Breathe deeply. Don't allow the puzzle to consume you and turn you into a puzzle-martyr. This is not what the *Zen of Puzzles* is all about. Having offered my last thought for the day, I'm going upstairs."

I smiled at her as she left and continued working the puzzle.

Chapter Eight

Finding a Way

Even though Grace warned me some puzzle pieces will seem to fit at least three other pieces, I did not face the problem until I began working on one of the smaller piles of mostly orange flowers. Many of them seemed to fit a number of other pieces—not just three—and after twenty fruitless minutes of not connecting anything, I felt myself getting frustrated. Really, really, really frustrated!

I pushed through and worked for another hour placing only three pieces. Martyr alert! I was obviously off-center and out of the flow so decided to stop and grab a cup of tea. I wandered into the kitchen and sat in the kitchen nook where I could watch the goings-on in the back garden. The sun was just beginning to make its way to the horizon through a break in the clouds. Long shadows striped a part of the garden in darkness and mottled other sections with wet light. Sheathed in drops of sunlit rain, the garden was no less than dazzling.

Through the closed windows, I could hear Canada geese honking high overhead, making their way south, flying under lines of towering clouds resolutely marching northward. I felt much calmer and registered how connecting with nature had very quickly re-centered me.

I thought about my work and the hours spent indoors while missing the beauty of this world. Feelings of sad regret sent me on a rapid slide into self-pity as a succession of mental pictures flooded my inner eye. I dwelled on times my work isolated me, and I began feeling oh-so-sorry for myself.

Thankfully, before too much time passed, I noticed my dismal state and realized *Reactive Rachel* had re-emerged with her usual song-and-dance. Off we went. However, having suspected she might return, I was able to mentally gallop in the opposite direction toward more positive and life-affirming images. *Responsive Rachel* with her posse came to the rescue and I began feeling much better.

In this feel-good flow of happier thoughts, I remembered a book I had read as a child. The main character was a paralyzed girl in an iron lung who connected with nature only through the narrow frame of her bedroom window. Through this portal, she would endlessly watch the changing sky and make up stories about flying among clouds or visiting far stars. The window gave the girl her own small piece of the heavens and she enjoyed the fascinating, ever changing complexity it revealed. She felt her life was full and rich.

While reading the book, I became more grateful for my many opportunities. I was humbled to realize how this child my own age had developed such a big love for all of life from so very little. I realized that I, with far greater access and mobility, had no business taking my own connection to nature for granted. I had totally forgotten my childhood wisdom before this kitchen conversation with myself.

I always knew nature fed my spirit, but what was I doing to maintain the connection? As I mulled over my always-indoor daytime routine, I realized all I had to do to stay linked was, at the very least, remember to look out a window and admire what I saw; take a fifteen-minute walk and enjoy being outside; or deeply and appreciatively breathe the air around me. By actively making these small changes, I could stay tuned in and in the flow.

Conscious puzzling. Conscious cooking. Conscious working. Conscious playing. Conscious living. It was all the same.

I understood I never needed to be disconnected unless I made the choice—consciously or unconsciously—to be disconnected, or if I allowed stress to catapult me into separated living. Remaining centered and aware was not impossibly complex. It would just require a whole lot of self-monitoring and practice.

I thought about the formula for being in the flow: remain conscious, be present with an open heart, play to re-center, and breathe. I could do that. I WOULD do that. The declaration loosened the last of my tight frustration that finally fell away, dropping with an imaginary thunk to the floor. I opened the back door, grinned maniacally, and kicked the self-pity out, my eyes following its path until it got lost among the acorns the storm had scattered. It was time to get back to the puzzle.

The Return

Seeing the puzzle pieces (and myself) in a whole new light and handling each with careful concentration, I managed to put two pieces together which pre-tea, I was absolutely certain fit each other, though I couldn't make them work. I decided to first try pieces looking like obvious fits. I put another two together, then another two, then another two. I repeated the process until before long, I joined these couplings to other puzzle pieces. I worked the puzzle with full confidence and total conviction. I was having fun again. I had found my way back into the flow.

When I could go no further with the pieces I felt sure about, I began to test those appearing iffy. These took a bit more patience. I held them; looked carefully at their shapes and colors; turned them to all angles; and tried their fit with other pieces. Slowly, one-by-one, patterns began to emerge. I saw I needed to replace a few pieces I had previously placed, but the rest looked fine.

I played with each puzzle piece and reminded myself it was okay if I ended up replacing it later. By giving myself permission to be wrong in the process of eventually getting it right, I worked without inner frustration—without drama. This approach to a project was very new and actually felt pretty good. Tingling with another *aha moment*, I realized that taking a considered hit-or-miss approach with a line-of-sight to a greater outcome is an acceptable and appropriate strategy. Ta-da! Another seismic shift.

At times, I might need to stop trying to figure everything out in advance, especially when standing at the shoreline of the unknown. I might just wade into the waters and sense the currents without having a clue about what to do next. I must trust—even if I can't see the other critters sharing the water with me—even if I'm not exactly sure how deep the water was going to get.

I didn't need to know all the small steps to get to where I'm going as long as I remained clear about my final destination. I could take my time and make decisions as I went along. I knew how to swim. If I got in over my head, I could always ask someone to throw me a lifeline.

New things, people, and events would always show up, and I would never figure out whether I liked or disliked them unless I tried them, knew them, and experienced them. So, why the heck not engage life more openly? Why not take more chances? All I had to do was keep my goal in sight—having a happier, fuller, and more interesting life, and maybe even playing more!

Okay. Deep breath. This was getting interesting.

Considering I had lived long enough to acquire a good dose of life experience, I knew I could handle almost any new or strange situation. To the patiently awaiting puzzle pieces I said out loud, "Yes, I *would* know what to do. I *will* always be okay." Having articulated my new awareness to the world, I resolved to allow more hit-or-misses and take it from there.

I completed the greater part of the mostly orange section before noticing several pieces in the center. Though they initially looked like they would fit, I could now see they were clearly misplaced. They needed to be removed. My mind jumped to the obvious parallels in my life. A floodgate opened. I was on a roll. Go, Rachel!

What served me well in one life stage may no longer serve in the next as new experiences led to growth and change and I became more aware. In the future, when my wiser, more experienced self suggested I move an outdated interpretation of my life to a less central spot, I must be willing to take action and change it. I was not wrong for originally placing it there (recalling Aunt Grace's crossword-puzzle analogy), but I would be foolish not to make the move.

The parallels to my marriage and divorce to Jonathan were obvious.

Making Room

Though I carefully removed the two pieces I wanted to change, I inadvertently pulled seven others out with them. I had somehow managed to find the only interlocking pieces in the entire puzzle, and their removal was rather awkward. I needed to put together the seven pieces again before finding a new home for the two I had orphaned. What a ridiculous waste of time.

Uh oh. Another martyr alert. Definitely not in the flow. Take another deep breath, girlfriend, and re-center. Better? Yes. Okay. Now continue.

What could I learn from this mishap? How could I reframe this puzzle experience to make it positive rather than wasteful? How could I apply this small lesson to my bigger life?

I sat with the seven pieces I had accidentally pulled out and an idea began to form. At first, I chased it away because it felt ridiculous. But since no one was around and this was a time for exploring seemingly crazy ideas, I boldly spoke directly to the puzzle pieces, "I'm holding one of the pieces to this puzzle section. Which of you wants to be the first to be reconnected?" My question sounded really strange, even to me, but as soon as I asked it, my eye automatically went to one of the remaining pieces. I felt a bit like a Twilight Zone walk-on when the piece fit perfectly with the first try.

I asked again, "Who would like to be placed next?" Then another piece seemed to call my attention, and I picked it up and easily connected it. When I asked the question a third time and had the same result, I started to get a little freaked out. What was happening? I finished connecting the other four pieces as easily and then returned the set of seven to the center of the puzzle section.

"Mamma mia!" as Gina would say. Mind-blowing. Did the response come from the puzzle pieces or from my subconscious mind? I couldn't wait to repeat the step and find out.

Apparently, the puzzle pieces responded in some degree to the attention I had focused on them and to my invitation to participate in my process. They became conscious/interactive when I bonded with them and treated them with appreciation and respect. I thought of another similar story that had made a deep impression—a story about a few of the old stone walls built hundreds of years ago in Hawaii, still whole and standing to this day.

I was told by a local Hawaiian guide that in the old days, when village walls were needed, the kahunas, the shamans or medicine men of the Hawaiian people, went into the fields and talked to the stones, asking which of them wanted to become part of the planned wall. Sensing the stones which responded affirmatively, the kahunas then directed the villagers to take only the stones they pointed out. These stones and no others were used to fashion the terraced walls—walls built without any binding substance between the stones.

Many Hawaiians thought this was why the walls continued to stand and hold strongly—because the stones had accepted an invitation long ago and freely chosen their destiny. Because of this, they still kept their promise to be part of a bigger purpose called *wall*.

Since hearing the story a few years ago, I began applying the principle of invitation to my grocery shopping. I positioned myself in front of the vegetables and fruits, mentally asking each type which were willing to come home to be eaten by me and offer their goodness by giving my body her needed fuel. After asking the questions, I found my eyes naturally went to certain vegetables and fruits, and after holding them and sensing their *rightness*, they became the purchased ones. When I did consume them, I thanked them for their willingness to support my well-being and blessed them on their way.

I would like to think I honored the produce by first asking for their assistance and by doing this, they would honor me as well by giving energy to my body and supporting my good health. I'd never really know if the invitation process worked, but I continued to do this small ritual. It just felt right and I was consistently full of energy and remained very healthy. The invitation certainly seemed to be working well.

Who Wants to Play?

When the thought about using the same technique with the puzzle pieces initially poked my memory, I was startled. A part of me still denied that giving honor through attention and invitation really made a difference, especially to inanimate puzzle pieces. But another part of me knew the truth of it. Could it be that the combination of invitation, rightness, and willingness influences everything? Were there clues here for how to relate to the world? Were these clues central to building connection, to building relationships, with both living and seemingly non-living things?

The thoughts kept coming—almost more than I could keep up with, they were firing so quickly. But I decided to just let them loose and see where they took me. Why not? Let's test the waters and see what happens when I waded in over my head. But first I needed to stretch.

Not to waste a minute, I stretched and reflected on my interactions with people. How did I know if I liked them when I first met them? How did I figure out if I wanted to see them again? How did acquaintances become friends? How was I sure of my attraction to a particular man and the right time to take him as a lover? What did all these people signal to initially get my attention? What did I signal back to get theirs?

In every scenario, I realized relationship-building first began with my placing attention on the other person so they knew they were *seen and accepted* as unique and individual. Once my attention was engaged, the next step became a spoken or an unspoken invitation to move forward in getting to know each other better. The initial recognition changed into expressed interest because of a sense of *rightness* with the relationship.

Though relationships took many forms, it seemed the initial attention first captured my mind or heart; the follow-up invitation; the sense of rightness; and my willingness to act were at the core when establishing relationships. I'd need to become more conscious of this dynamic and honor it, just as I had honored these seven puzzle pieces that readily came together.

Could it really be this simple? If it worked for puzzle pieces, why would attention, invitation, rightness, and willingness to act not work for everyone and everything?

Stretching done, I walked to the window and watched crows playing on the wind. The rain had diminished a little but the wind still blew hard. The crows whipped by so quickly, they appeared elongated, stretched by their rocketing G-force. I read their Morse code of black dots and dashes before they disappeared from view. I wished I could play on the wind with them.

On a tangent, I thought about how in this no-pain-no-gain society, we were somehow deceived into believing in the noble struggle. We valued only results produced by hard work, iron discipline, and decisive action. We rewarded those who overcame huge obstacles. Even when our personal circumstances don't necessitate such a struggle, we kept trying to prove our worthiness (or perhaps our superiority) to both ourselves and others.

But whose script were we following? Whose blueprint? Why were we suspicious if success came along too easily? Whatever happened to ease and elegance? Whatever happened to grace? (Pun intended.)

I was a great believer in the hero's journey with challenges making me stronger. However, fighting dragons was one thing, but getting seriously burned or even killed in the process was quite another. How could I reframe my internal hero's journey and make it less desperate and emotionally dangerous? Was calling on my warrior aspect the answer? How did all of this relate to the flow?

I really liked the idea of being centered and remaining in the flow. I knew exactly what Grace meant when she talked about it, and I could think of many times I was both in and way out of the flow. Conscious living could keep me there, where I wanted to be. Why did I invest so much in the struggle? Why did I think I needed to *earn* my way to ease and grace when they're natural gifts available to everyone? Was I trying to live as a noble martyr, ready to victimize myself for the greater good? More things to think about while running

Since I now understood attention, invitation, rightness, and willingness to act, I completed the orange-and-yellow flower section within the next half hour and connected it to the red section. I was very satisfied when I realized I had tapped into a truth much greater than puzzling. I stretched one more time before going upstairs to change for dinner.

What an intriguing time. What other games were afoot? Look sharp, Sherlock.

Chapter Nine

The Tools of Attention

Dinner at our favorite local restaurant was excellent, and we returned to the house feeling very relaxed and satisfied. I went upstairs to change into something sloppy and comfortable and then met a dressed-for-sleep Grace as she was leaving her room to come down for a final cup of tea. Grace was wearing a simple pair of pale rose lounging pajamas instead of her usual dripping-with-lace night garb. She had almost gone native. I sincerely hoped I could take credit for being a bad influence.

Grace was up for a bit of puzzling as was I. I wanted to start working on the last flower section of mostly yellow blooms. Since she had not yet completed the stream section, she said my focusing on the yellows was fine with her.

I built a fire, brewed a pot of tea, and brought the pot and two cups into the sunroom. Grace poured for us both before sitting. But instead of concentrating on her section, she placed her laser focus on how I was working the puzzle. I found this unusual attention a tad unnerving and began feeling very self-conscious. What was she thinking? Not good. When I looked up, I could see Grace knew exactly why I stopped working. The pouncing gleam was back in her eyes again and she was grinning. In the flickering flames, she looked strangely like the tea-partying Mad Hatter I had dreamed about.

"What?" I asked. "Why are you smiling? I know you're just dying to say something."

"Oh, did I make you nervous?"

"You know you did," I laughingly retorted. "I felt like you were trying to break my concentration. Were you?"

Grace gave me her wide-eyed-innocent-who-me look, and I knew I had guessed correctly. She tried to keep a straight face, but ended up chuckling instead.

"I just wanted to see what would happen if I watched you while you worked the puzzle. You were concentrating fully on what you were doing until you let yourself become distracted, and then you lost your connection with the pieces. I knew the exact second you took your attention from the pieces and placed it instead on me.

"In a millisecond, you ceased referencing the puzzle and alternatively, began referencing your own inner state. You wondered what I was thinking about you and if I were judging your puzzling skills. You began worrying about your own performance. Is this typical behavior for you?"

"Merde!" was my mental response. I learned this handy expletive when I was with Grace and George in France. Ah, the joys of a classical education.

Curiouser and Curiouser

"Huh?" was my dumb verbal response. So much for the classical education. Wishing to sound just a little more intelligent, I answered with my own question. "Do what a lot?" giving her my wide-eyed-innocent-who-me look I had picked up from her. "You mean the attention part?"

"No, the performance part. Reflecting on what just happened, can you understand how moving your attention and connection from your heart to your head led to concerns about your performance—how you were being evaluated and judged by someone else? Do you see the link between being concerned about performance and narrowing your infinite potential by fitting it into an external standard of rights and wrongs? When you make love, where do you put your attention?"

Totally surprised, I almost snorted tea from my nose before barely managing to swallow. Charming. Grace's out-of-the-blue question totally threw me, and I delayed answering for a few seconds so I would sound more like a grown-up than a shocked adolescent.

"You've asked an interesting question. When I made love with Jonathan, someone I knew very well and was comfortable with, my focus and attention were on us both. I remained fully aware of and enjoyed the pleasure he was giving me, but I also got great pleasure from seeing how good I was making him feel. We were totally connected and mindful of each other. There actually wasn't a whole lot of thought going on. I let my love for him fall into a whole-body feeling state and let love take me where it would. However, toward the end of the marriage everything changed and I could sense, though we were still having sex, we certainly weren't making love. Is this what you were asking?"

"Mostly. But think about when you're with someone new. Are you as comfortable? Where's your focus then?"

Since I had never really thought about this before, I turned each question over in my mind, holding them at arm's length in case they decided to bite me.

"Here goes. I'm not sure if this is what you're asking. I'll keep questioning until I understand where you're trying to go with this.

"In my pre-Jonathan days, when I was first getting to know a new man I'd like to date for a while, I was more in my head than in my heart when we were in bed. I paid close attention to what turned him on, and I carefully observed how I responded when he did the same for me. There was more an emphasis on pleasing the other person and being pleased rather than relaxing into real pleasure. Effortless pleasure came when I knew him better and all of me was engaged. In the beginning, I guess both of us were more in our heads and focusing on performance.

"Maybe that's why the question 'Was it good for you?' has become a standard after-sex question. We want a report card on how we performed.

"However, there were times when I was younger and enjoyed uncomplicated, recreational sex. It was fun. I learned a lot. If I wanted to, I could easily move to the next lover. No strings, no entanglements.

"Now that I know more about myself, though, I'm just not as interested in going to bed with strangers. I'd like to get to know a guy before I sleep with him. When I have sex with a man I relate to, I stay out of my head and feel more trusting and relaxed. My heart is more present to my partner and to myself. Of course, there are some interesting exceptions.

"A few times while I was still dating, I met men I'd instantly and totally lusted for. Lord, how they turned me on. When I had sex with them, it was pretty primal and mind-blowing. There were no thoughts whatsoever going on in my head. Nothing existed except my overwhelming need to have my sexual hunger satisfied—and satisfied immediately and fully. My body said I must have him then and there or die trying. All I remember from these times was feeling a devouring heat and a lashing urgency driving me wild. I'm smiling just thinking of a few of those rides. I'm probably blushing too. Unbelievable.

"Of course, this kind of sex is much different from making love with a heart connection, but it certainly has its place. Jonathan and I experienced some pretty lusty primal times as well, especially during make-up and fantasy sex. I was totally out of control with the intensity of it and this was just fine with me. Maybe I'm giving you more than you asked for, but there you have it."

Grace reached over and patted my hand. I guess I'd done just fine.

"Actually, I'm very happy you experienced the out-of-control times—your primal times, as you called them—

which a lot of women never let themselves enjoy. Men don't have a real problem with primal because they're more directly wired to their sexuality and often do what comes naturally without a whole lot of thought. Therefore, early in their sexual histories, after they've learned the basics of sex and developed their *moves*, men don't usually think about performance if everything is functioning well—just their own satisfaction. If they're adult men, though, and not still emotional little boys, and if they care about the person they're with, then they also focus on their partner's satisfaction.

"All goes well for men until they begin to age and parts stop working the way they used to. This doesn't need to be a huge issue for them if they have the right partners who show them how they both can be inventive with their hands and mouths. Some men can let those alternatives be okay. Some can't. They just cannot get beyond the performance part, the proving-I'm-sill-a-man part. Again, it depends on how mature and self-confident they are.

"On the other hand, women, even if they initially begin their lovemaking with a heart connection, can easily get distracted and go into their heads. The craziest thoughts might intrude at the most intimate moments, usually a list of things they need to do or concerns about work or children. This distracted state does not arise from performance issues, but from the loss of centeredness and attention on the other.

"Also, there are women who do not allow themselves to get lost in sex. They might have suffered traumatic sexual experiences in the past. Perhaps they have been taught this level of passion is sinful. Or maybe they think, consciously or unconsciously, that by withholding sex, they can control their partners. This gives these women a false sense of power, and they might even feel superior to what they judge to be the *weak male*. But, these women are missing the heights and depths of their own sexual pleasure, or their own humanity. I'm delighted you've known the freedom and passion these women deny themselves.

"You've heard that fires initially blazing too soon, too fast, or too hot, burn themselves out very quickly? This is mostly true, and this concept can also be applied to lovemaking. Hot and primal might not last and could even burn. For the longer-term, you need the balance of both your mind and heart to engage in the *slow burn*, the steady constant of loving endurance. Make no mistake, though. You also need healthy doses of the hot burn to keep it interesting.

"Remember—there are no right and wrong ways for adults to make love or to have sex with other consenting adults. All the pleasure you'll ever experience will come to you through the gift of your body, so enjoy it for the marvel it is. Just be sure you're always thoroughly honest with yourself and respectful of your partner in deciding what you will or will not do. Live by your truth according to your consciously chosen values and beliefs. This doesn't mean you must always be in a lofty, conscious space. Sex can simply be plain, mindless pleasure. Find your own balance and your own mix.

"Notice that where you put your focus and attention during lovemaking often mirrors where you put your focus and attention in other areas of life. When making love, are you impatient? Giving? Cruel? Controlled? Kind? Adventurous? Mechanical? Hurried? Selfish? Playful? There are legions of adjectives I could use. If you think about your sexual experiences with different partners, you can probably make a connection between the way they make love and the way they generally deal with people. It's a fascinating study.

"Watch yourself as you move through the routine of your days and notice where you place your focused attention. If you wish to live life with genuine passion, stay centered in mind and heart, be fully present to whatever you're doing and those you're doing it with. If this is true for your life, it will be true for your lovemaking. That's all I have to say about that.

"I thought it might be fun just to see what happened when I watched you. I found this exercise to be most informative, and I hope you can say the same."

The Noble Quest

I was a bit speechless and did not reply, just stared at her blankly. Having accomplished her mission and finished her tea, Grace turned her entire attention to the puzzle and proceeded to complete the stream section she worked on earlier. She let me know she would focus on the blue border flowers the next day. I returned to puzzling as well and did a bit of parallel mental puzzling about what she had said.

We both remained quiet, each concentrating on the puzzle and focusing inward. We peacefully listened to the crackle of the fire as logs collapsed and spit embers. From time to time as a gust hit the roof, the wind reached down the chimney and flames leaped to grab it. Very dramatic. At one point, Gus wandered in and lay on my feet. The sound of high winds unsettled him a bit and this was his way of finding safety.

Suddenly Grace shouted, "There you are!" so loudly, Gus and I both jumped. I didn't bark as he did though I did yelp once. "I thought I lost you, and now here you are" she cooed as she put the final piece into the center of her now-completed stream section.

"Why are you shouting?" I asked ungraciously, "and why are you talking out loud to the puzzle pieces?" Gus got disgusted by the disturbance and left, seeking quieter shelter.

Grace grinned once again and replied, "I'm talking to the puzzle pieces because it's what you told me you did earlier. Remember? They seem to like it when I talk to them. As far as the shouting, I got a bit carried away. I've been looking for this puzzle piece for hours, and I could swear I'd lost it. Sorry.

"But do you remember when we talked about how the mind filters everything and makes us perceive things in certain ways? Well, I guess my *expectation* about what this piece *should* look like created a filter keeping me from immediately seeing it. I ended up finding the piece in a completely different color pile, one I never would have thought to check before. When I noticed it sitting directly on top like it was waiting to be discovered, I wondered how I'd not noticed it since it was such an obvious fit. I got excited when I dropped my filter and could see the piece clearly. I always feel like I'm making progress when that happens.

"Whew! Enough excitement for me for one night. I'm going to have one more cup of tea with you and then go to bed."

While sipping her tea, Grace sat and watched as I worked on completing the bottom half of my section. I was almost done and only a few more pieces remained, but like Grace, I was stuck on finding one last piece. This time, though, as she watched, I did not get into my head or allow performance issues to bubble up. I just kept working.

I lined up about fifteen possible pieces in front of me which might fit an open spot near the edge of the section. I took each piece and tried it on every side before putting the already-tried piece into a discard pile. I picked up piece after piece until there were eleven left to try, then eight, then four, then none. I looked through other color piles. Nothing. I asked the missing piece to show itself, to talk to me. Silence. I could feel myself getting frustrated again. I did not care if I needed to stay at this table all night—I was determined to complete this freakin' section.

Grace said nothing except, "Did I ever tell you the

story of the warm pebble?" When I shook my head *no*, she continued. "It's a Zen teaching story you'll understand right away. I heard it years ago and have never forgotten it."

She sat a little straighter, folded her hands like an orator, and began.

"One day, a Zen teacher brought his student to the edge of a rocky beach in winter and said, 'Somewhere on this beach is a pebble you'll find warm to the touch. It will offer you enlightenment. You must find the pebble and bring it to me.' Without saying anything further, the teacher turned and walked away. The student was not daunted by his task even though the beach was quite large. He was resolved on finding the pebble quickly and impressing his teacher with both his competence and his persistence.

"The student first studied the beach to determine whether the sun would make one part warmer than the others. When he realized the entire beach lay under the shadow of a tall mountain, he knew he would find no obvious clues. He walked onto the beach and immediately began his quest. As he moved to the water's edge, the student decided to throw any discarded pebbles into the ocean to prevent mistakenly checking any pebble twice.

"Quickly getting into a rhythm, the student methodically moved from one section of the beach to the next. Bend over. Pick up a pebble. Sense it. Throw it into the ocean. Bend over. Pick up a pebble. Sense it. Throw it into the ocean. This went on for hours and hours until the student became tired and hungry, but he did not stop. Bend over. Pick up a pebble. Sense it. Throw it into the ocean.

"Even more hours passed, and the student's back was aching; his hand was raw; his throwing arm and shoulder hurt; and he was ravenously hungry. Still he endured and pressed on. Bend over. Pick up a pebble. Sense it. Throw it into the ocean. Again and again—without pause or rest.

"The day passed slowly until the sun told the boy it was already late afternoon. He began to wonder when he would finally complete this impossible task. He thought about the meals he had missed and about the one he would enjoy when he returned. He thought about how proud his teacher would be when he brought him the warm pebble. He shivered when he realized how cold he would get if his task continued into the night.

"Thoughts tumbled around the student's head, one dragging another with it. All the student could think about was how miserable he felt, but when he remembered he was pursuing enlightenment, he became even more determined to find the warm pebble. Wiping his sweating forehead, he said to himself, 'Just one more pebble and then another and another.' Almost magically, when the student next bent over to pick up a pebble, he discovered it was warm. However, instead of putting it into the pocket of his robe, he reflexively threw it into the ocean and stood dismayed, not sure what to do next.

"Everything crashed inside and he felt slightly ill. 'What have I just done? Why did I throw away the warm pebble? How will I ever find enlightenment now? What will I tell my teacher?'

"With a heavy heart, the student trudged home. When he arrived, the teacher was expectantly waiting for him but before he could say anything, the teacher offered a cup of cold water. 'Drink' the teacher said. 'Quench your thirst after all your fine effort.'

"Then the teacher gave his student a plate of food—much more than usual—his favorite foods—prepared exactly the way he liked them. The student started to protest, but the teacher simply raised his index finger, shook his head back and forth, and gave him the plate. 'No. Do not speak. I told the cook to prepare this food especially for you. Eat and refresh yourself after working so diligently all day to find the warm pebble of enlightenment.'

"The student felt terrible. He had utterly failed in his task. All he wanted to do was tell his teacher what happened, but the teacher again shook his head and pointed to the food. Even though these were his favorite foods, they tasted like dust. Obediently but morosely, the student ate every crumb. When he finished his meal, the teacher said, 'Now you may speak. Tell me how you successfully found the warm pebble.'

"Well, the student was mortified. What was he going to say? Hanging his head, he told his teacher everything, explaining how he had found the warm pebble but threw it away. He had failed. He would never find enlightenment. All his efforts were fruitless. The teacher was silent for a few seconds and then asked, 'But what have you learned?'

"Trying to redeem himself if only a little, the student replied, 'Teacher, I have learned many things. I learned when I allowed my thoughts to distract me from what I was doing, I stopped honoring the pebble I held. The distractions made it too easy for me to reflexively throw the warm pebble away when I found it. I was so caught up in my own discomfort and mindless repetition, I lost sight of the task's purpose and began to resent how hungry and sore it was making me. Finally, I wanted to show you how clever I was and, instead, my pride led me astray. I stand before you humbled and contrite. I am sorry, teacher, for failing to bring you the warm pebble of enlightenment. I will leave this place without complaint if you say I must.'

"The student stood miserably as one painful minute after another passed, waiting to hear his fate. When the teacher began laughing, the startled student looked up with a question in his eyes. 'You have missed the point,' said the teacher. 'The warm pebble could not bring you enlightenment, but the conscious search for it would and did. You now are more aware of when and under what circumstances your focus and attention can stray. You understand how unconscious routines might numb you. You have seen how your pride can drive you as crazy as a monkey with fleas. You have learned how worrying about the opinions of others can keep you from enjoying what you are doing. You are on the path to enlightenment, my student, because you allowed a small pebble to teach you big lessons. I am most pleased.'

"The astonished student looked carefully into the eyes

of his teacher and understanding flowed into him. The answers were not found *outside* himself, though external hints could point to the truths he already carried *inside* himself. This was a lesson he would never forget. The student had succeeded in finding a warm pebble of enlightenment. He had just confused *doing* something to achieve enlightenment with *being* enlightened. Having gained greater wisdom, the student thanked his teacher and followed him into the temple.

"And they lived happily ever after. The end."

Keeping the Warm Pebble

I laughed at the way Grace finished the story but told her I totally understood the moral of this wonderful teaching and warmly thanked her like the student had thanked his own teacher. "If you grasped the meaning of this story, then prove it," she said, "and find your missing piece."

Nothing like a little pressure. "Here goes nothing," I thought.

I gathered the pieces in the discard pile and began trying them one more time. Since my attention was now centered on the piece—not on the task—not on the completion—not on my frustration—not on Grace's opinion—I quickly found it. Thinking of the student, I picked up a puzzle piece I had initially discarded, and with a sense of triumph, I placed it in the empty space.

The Force was with me that evening. Beaming with victory, as if I had just single-handedly blown up the

Death Star, I gazed at the puzzle with great approval knowing this part was finally complete. "Now I understand why you shouted," I grinned at Grace. (A lot of grinning was going on.)

"Good job, Rachel!" my Aunt Yoda proudly responded.

We sat for a few minutes admiring our work. We talked a little about how the patterns of the puzzle were becoming more evident as we completed each section. The puzzle was now a little over half finished. Grace reminded me to continue asking my subconscious to work with me as I slept. Then she kissed me good night and went upstairs.

I didn't want to work on the puzzle any longer. I embraced my time of enlightenment and it was enough for one evening. I looked in the living room where my mother sat reading in front of a roaring fire. I grinned (another grin!) when I noticed Gus on his back in front of the flames, dream running in his sleep. I returned to the sunroom; poured the last cup of tea; closed the fireplace flue; turned off the lights; and joined Mom in the living room.

She looked up and said hello when I sat in a chair next to where she was comfortably stretched on the sofa. She put her book down and looked at me asking with sincere interest how the puzzling was going. We talked late into the night.

Chapter Ten

The Middle and the End

I woke to the sound of rain still percussing the roof. No run this morning. "Thank goodness—an idle, guilt-free morning," I thought as I snuggled under the comforter. An hour later, the rain was still in full orchestra mode, trying to lullaby me back into sleep, but it was time to get out of bed. My morning coffee was calling. I showered, dressed, and made my way downstairs to find coffee, but no sign of anyone else. Not a creature was stirring, not even a Gus.

I carried my mug into the living room to discover someone had made a fire with apple wood and the sweet smell filled the room. Lovely.

Picking up a nubby green-and-gold throw, I moved to the window seat snugged into the bay window. Wrapping the blanket around me, I settled to watch the storm.

The wilder aspects of nature always blissed me out and the whipping rain of this nor'easter continued to put on quite a show. The ocean was frothed like the best cappuccino. I found the view delicious.

I did not want to think deep thoughts. I just hoped everything would click together and my subconscious would do its thing without too much effort on my part. After the previous day's emotional high, having a bit of the mundane actually felt much more relaxing. Of course, I had tried this leave-me-alone approach yesterday, but hopefully I would have better luck with it today.

One cup of coffee led to another. An hour later I heard movement upstairs, a signal to begin preparing breakfast for whoever might show up. A slow morning. An easy, lazy morning. No one appeared, but I made another pot of coffee, put breakfast in the buffet warmers, and grabbed a third cup before heading toward the sunroom. It was definitely a fireplace day, and I started a fire (with apple wood, of course) before sitting at the table to work the puzzle.

Making My Way

The puzzle was about three-quarters complete though we still needed to work on the sky and all the pieces adjoining the border. The hill of wildflowers and the stream were now finished and I sat for a few minutes admiring all the pieces coming together in such vivid detail. Grace had been correct. Just looking at the puzzle brought back such wonderful memories of the meadow where we passed an afternoon with food and conversation. I could feel my heart smiling, though the tug of missing Uncle George came with it.

Four piles of greens waited to be placed as well as three piles of grays and browns. Grass and boulders. Blues of sky. I naturally gravitated to the greens, the hopeful color of spring and new beginnings. I worked through one pile and was pulling another toward me when Grace came into the room. We exchanged good-mornings; Grace thanked me for making breakfast; and we turned to the serious play of puzzling.

The sounds of wind, rain, and fire created an audio backdrop. The creaks of the house added harmony. Looking across at this woman who had held one of the central places in my life for such a long time, I was again filled with gratitude and wonder at my good fortune. Grace must have sensed my wave of high emotion. She smiled, reached over, patted my hand, and kept working/playing. All was well.

Temperature Check

We stayed at it for a little longer, continuing to make a lot of progress. At this rate, we would complete the puzzle by the following morning, and we'd have time to take a break before Robert and Gina came late Friday afternoon. I was focused on the third green pile when Grace said, "Did you notice a change in your energy when we got to the middle of the puzzle yesterday?"

I paused a beat and said, "Quite honestly, I was getting a little tired of puzzling and being constantly bombarded by new thoughts. After putting our attention on it for days, I felt both physically and emotionally challenged. I'm not accustomed to sitting for this long and inactivity is hard on my body. At a deeper level, all the parallels you've been making between puzzling and real life began to boggle my mind while, at the same time, stretch my heart—not always a comfortable process. Though we'd completed more than half the puzzle, there was still a long way to go. I guess all of a sudden, I got a bit weary of putting all my energy there."

"How do you feel this morning?"

I hesitated again to really sense my feelings, wanting to be sure I could give her my most honest answer.

"I slept longer than usual—pure luxury. I love sitting and watching the rain and I took a little time to enjoy the storm. I realized my Type A personality had bitten me in the butt and turned puzzling into a task rather than an activity giving me pleasure. I recognized I'd let the glass-half-empty perspective grab me. Therefore, instead of thinking about how much of the puzzle still needed to be worked, I shifted my focus to how much we've already accomplished.

"In an instant, I changed my point of view to glass-half-full and I became interested in getting back to the puzzle again to see how it all turned out. In fact, since many pieces have already been placed, I'm finding this last quarter of the puzzle is moving much more quickly. To answer your question, at this point I feel great, but I would have given you a different answer three hours ago. Is this what you were asking?"

"Yes, I wanted to check with you because in the middle of any process, I get the same way. When I've been working on a project with great intensity and intimacy, I tend to get tired at some point in the middle. It's like I've launched my sailboat into a wide bay on my way to the opposite shore."

I smiled. She knew I loved water analogies and she was offering another. Grace smiled back and continued.

"Like clockwork, at a point in the middle of the bay, the wind of my energy dies down and I feel like I'm going nowhere. I can't see the shore where I first launched and the shore I'm headed toward is not yet in sight. If I'm not careful, I can get exhausted or discouraged.

"Having experienced this anomaly often enough, though, I can recognize what it is, and I've learned to give myself a few time-outs. When I feel like I've hit a wall, I simply remind myself I've entered the predictable *mid-process blahs* and then move on, knowing I can shift my perspective and become re-energized just like you figured out how to do this morning. The winds will return and I will sail to project's end. Chocolate also helps."

I laughed out loud at that one.

"The *blahs* can show up when you've been working through an issue with someone; when you've been in a relationship for a while; and when a project lasts for a long time. You can add anything to this list. The point I'm trying to make is, if you anticipate and recognize this very human part of a process, you can then manage it with greater ease. It's up to each of us to change perspective and rededicate ourselves to the process, relationship, or project at hand. Do you agree?"

"Well, I've never really thought about it, but based on the mental gymnastics I did with myself this morning, I absolutely agree. When I sat with the puzzle this morning, I was able to appreciate where the process is leading us rather than grumbling about how long it's taken to get here. Though I must say, it also felt good to mentally use several creative curses to scare the junky stuff from my thoughts. Not as good as chocolate, but definitely effective."

It was her turn to laugh out loud. "Yes, I do understand. Since I have now delivered the morning insight, why don't we take a breakfast break? I'm hungry!"

We enjoyed breakfast while the rest of the household slept. A lazy day for everyone. After cleaning up, we puzzled for a few hours, continuing to enjoy the quiet. By that time, everyone had appeared to say good morning before eating their own breakfasts and scattering to take care of business. We decided to gather later for lunch.

A meal with my family has been likened to a synchronized swimming event which friends enjoy watching and cheering on. We each knew our parts after years of practice and performed integrated patterns of preparing, cooking, eating, and washing up with little thought and effort. I guess we had become pretty good at the meal event because we regularly received at least a 9.6 score from the judges even without gelling our hair.

My father and Gus descended from the office and my mother returned from taking care of a few ultra-secret, last-minute party details. During lunch, we spent a pleasant hour catching up on each other's comings and goings before separating again to complete our afternoon missions.

Grace went upstairs afterwards to check on business items, and I thought Antonio might be part of that business. Sweet. I decided to continue puzzling and skip a potential run despite Gus's muttering and dashing back and forth to the front door, looking meaningfully in my direction. Not very subtle, our Gus.

Before departing, Grace reviewed section #377b of the *Master Puzzler's Rule Book* stating one puzzler would not complete the puzzle without the others who worked it. It further stated that respecting the rules of puzzling would result in a positive bottom line for everyone. Yes, she was definitely in business mode.

Not a problem. We still had a few hours to go.

Shifting Winds

All the grassy green pieces were complete and I began attaching the different sections, placing them in the larger puzzle. I loved the resulting satisfaction when all the little sections I worked on came together to form a larger whole. From my new vantage point, I could appreciate the puzzle process with all its implied teachings.

"Oh, no. There goes my mind again, and I didn't want to think lofty thoughts today," I mentally groaned as the parallels to my life began to intrude. I ignored them.

I decided to next turn my attention to the yellows. Grace had started the browns and, therefore, I would leave those for her. We were humming along and would definitely be finished tomorrow.

Grace came down, kissed my cheek, and continued to work on her browns as I continued playing with the yellows. Before she became too deeply engrossed I said, "I'm still surprised at how quickly I was able to put these pieces together now that my puzzle options are fewer. And, yes, I can see it in your eyes. There's a lesson here. Okay. Just for you, Aunt Grace. Here's what I'm thinking.

"I need to look at all my options right now and this can become confusing, but I know choosing a new direction will get easier once I narrow my possibilities—just like it's becoming easier to find puzzle pieces because there aren't as many to sort through. I also know my parts of the puzzle were completed only after I became willing to try different fits and make mistakes. However, making mistakes feels so much riskier when I think about starting all over and maybe making another wrong choice.

"I just need my heart to catch up with my mind. I know no experience is ever wasted and one thing can lead to another in right order and perfect timing if I remain conscious. But I get scared. My heart still screams its *what ifs*.

"Changing my mind has always felt to me like failing, but I'm learning not to be so hard on myself. I finally figured out changing directions rather than sticking stubbornly to what's not working is a healthier approach to life.

I guess my divorce actually taught me this lesson. Anyway, I remember a statement my mother would loosely quote from Erma Bombeck, an American humorist, when I complained about my most recent screw-up. She would say, 'Don't worry about it, Rachel. Remember, even if you try something new and fall flat on your face, you're still a body length ahead.'"

We both chuckled. Grace said, "On this lighter note, I think we should stop for the day. We have only a few more hours of working the puzzle and I want us to really savor them tomorrow."

Just two unworked sections remained and eight to ten odd single pieces. "We're quickly approaching step *eight*—the completion of the puzzle," Grace said. "How are you feeling?"

"Actually, if a few glasses of wine were in me, I might be just a little weepy. I cannot begin to tell you how much this time with you has meant. I feel like you've helped me grow a decade's worth in the last few days. As always, you've handed me important life tools. But most importantly, I feel like you've passed your mantle, your legacy, to me whether this was your intention or not. It's like you've given me an early inheritance wrapped in your heart and soul. How can I even assign a value to what you've done for me or begin to express how much you mean to me?" Even without the wine, I teared up.

In a nanosecond, we both became a little weepy. "Let's shut down everything here and get a glass of wine," I said, "Then we can do this leaking part properly."

My parents joined us in the living room, carrying their drinks along with things for us to snack on. We decided to send out for Chinese and ended up drinking a little too much wine and eating a little too much food. We sat for hours in front of the fire and discussed everything from why camels spit to fossil fuel alternatives. It was a fascinating, funny, and heartfelt evening—one of the best.

Morning Will Come

Needless to say, we all slept soundly and, once again, I woke up late the following morning. I could still hear the rain on the roof, but the wind seemed to have lost a little of its punch. I guessed the nor'easter was finally blowing itself out and we might even have a beautiful sunset. With that happy thought, I rolled over and went back to sleep.

Later, I was the one who came downstairs after everyone else, and served myself breakfast from the warmer. It appeared my family had been up for hours and I was the last to roll out of bed. I could live with that.

I cleaned up the kitchen and put everything away before Dad came in for another cup of coffee. Since the tail-end of the storm had arrived, he was going to meet friends for lunch and then play a few games of indoor tennis. I was glad he was taking a break from work. I asked about Mom and Grace, and he said they had gone shopping because, at the last minute, my mother decided she wanted to buy something new for the party. Grace immediately declared she was going with her to ensure

Mom purchased something slightly indecent. He raised one eyebrow at this last statement, then smiling secretly, walked out the back door to check the fence, coffee mug in hand, leaving the door open a little for Gus to follow.

Gus looked at me inquiringly, moving his eyes from me to the door, but I told him, "No walk. No run." He looked at me with pity as he does when I'm being lazy, huffed twice, turned tail, and, defeated, decided to follow my father.

I took my coffee to the sunroom and rejoined the puzzle. The heavy clouds were lifting, and it was lighter outside. The storm was seriously thinking about being done with us.

By the time my mother and Grace returned, just one large gray section still needed to come together and be added to the rest. But I took a break and went upstairs to preview my mother's new dress she seemed a little unsure about for some reason. What have you done, Aunt Grace?

I asked Mom to model the emerald-green, floor-length gown Grace had found for her. The color made her green eyes glow and highlighted the red undertones of her auburn hair. She looked stunning and I told her so. "But why were you so hesitant about this dress?" I asked. Without commenting, she simply turned around.

The gown plunged dramatically in the back and my mother thought it showed too much skin for a woman her age. I said her back was wonderfully sculpted and she should flaunt what she had for as long as she had it. Knowing I would not flatter her or be dishonest, my mother finally agreed she would wear the dress and actually giggled about what my father would say when he saw her in it.

I never heard my mother giggle before. I knew she was enjoying feeling slightly wicked. Go, Mom! What a party this was shaping up to be.

We spent the next half hour selecting jewelry to show off both my mother and the dress. I could not wait to see everyone's reactions on Saturday. I erupted in giggles as well. (Really, Rachel? Giggles?) Saying I could visualize the happy, but somewhat surprised look on my father's face when he saw her in the dress, laughter erupted from us both. This was going to be good.

I went downstairs to congratulate Grace on her choice. In fact, I was truly dumbfounded she managed to talk my conservative mother into buying such a beautifully revealing dress. Then again, this was Aunt Grace working her usual magic.

Finish Line

Aunt Grace and I made our way into the sunroom and stood arm-in-arm, looking at the puzzle, realizing it would be completed within the hour. We smiled at each other and began working together on the last gray section and kept at it until only one piece remained. With a flourish, Grace gave me the honor of completing the puzzle.

It was done! I just sat there, not quite knowing what to do. It felt like I was waking from a pleasant dream. I couldn't figure out if I were glad to be done or wanted to start all over again, like craving second helpings of chocolate lava cake when I was already full. Then Grace loudly clicked her fingers under my nose and said, "Come back, Rachel. We're not quite finished. We still have a few things to do. It's time to move to the completion of step *eight*."

In turn, I snapped back to attention asking, "What's the rest of step *eight*? I thought we were finished."

"We completed the puzzle but not the process. Let's do it together right now. To finish step *eight*, we honor the puzzle we've spent so much time with as well as the effort it took us to complete it. We thank it for offering us needed teachings. Concluding step *eight*, then, is taking the time to admire our handiwork and enjoying our success. Let's take step *eight* now."

We stood in front of the puzzle with our arms around each other's waist and focused on the gorgeous scene spreading before us. We reminisced about the tougher sections and re-experienced our sense of accomplishment when sections finally came together. Our conversation led to memories of the vacation in France which inevitably brought happy thoughts of Uncle George. We savored the time, sipping it slowly, wrapped in reverie and appreciation.

"Now I want you to go upstairs and complete step *nine*—looking at what you learned and making the experience real to you," Grace instructed. "Too often in our hectic world, we quickly move from one important project or event to the next until everything becomes a blur.

It's like taking exquisite jewelry and heaping it in a pile, making it impossible to enjoy the distinct beauty of each piece. To fully appreciate the jewelry, it's best to display individual pieces where they can be seen and admired.

"The same holds true for projects and experiences. Don't just jumble them up in a pile without ever examining them, without creating space in between. When an ending comes, take the time to reflect on the experience and notice what you've learned or enjoyed. Savor the moment before letting it go. Impress into memory what you choose to hold onto and then forget the rest.

"Taking the time to be fully present to an experience helps you gain the wisdom integral to every part of your life if you let it have value and meaning. Why not do this now while I answer some phone messages and rest. Remember, step *nine* is about appreciation and honoring—the puzzle, your puzzling partners, and most importantly, yourself."

It sounded like a good plan to me. I went upstairs to my bedroom and sat in a chair in front of a side window offering a different view of the ocean. Gus heard me on the stairs and I let him in when he kept butting his head against the door. He bounded into the room, tail waving, and curled up on the window seat, possessing it like a king on his throne. Sighing happily, he fell asleep.

The rain, a mere patter earlier, was now a torrential downpour—the storm's last blast before retreating. I hope Dad was okay in the city. When it finally cleared, I would take a walk on the beach and give Gus a good run. He came out of his sound sleep and looked up as if reading my mind.

Pulling out my journal, I summarized all the thoughts and insights I had since the last time I wrote. Once complete, I put the journal aside and let my mind go blank while I watched the last of the rain. Probably no sunset later. Probably no run. Poor Gus.

This had been a really good time for me—almost a time-out-of-time—when I was removed from the normal-and-usual. I cannot say I received any immediate answers about what was next in my life, but I gained invaluable tools to help me get there. The patterns definitely became clearer. I felt I was seeing the world from a different perspective. As if an inner storm had passed through me while the outer storm raged, I was scrubbed-clean and ready for what was next. Perhaps I was even beginning to look forward to it.

Maybe this was the reason I had instinctively chosen to look out a side window with its changed ocean view. I liked what I was seeing, both inside and out. I would continue to welcome the new range of options presenting themselves, and I would ask my subconscious to help me put them into some kind of order. Because Aunt Grace had midwifed this new outlook, I believed with all my heart this would all happen as planned.

Party On

I must have dozed because I woke with a start when Mom knocked and let me know dinner was ready. No run on the beach. Oh well. It was still raining and this somewhat justified my be-lazy decision.

Before I came fully awake, though, I remembered a half-dream of standing in a grand ornate hallway with a number of doors on either side. As I walked by each door, it automatically opened for me without any effort on my part and light spilled from inside. I relished what my subconscious had communicated and got the message loud and clear. The hall of many beautiful options.

I opened the bedroom door to let Gus gallop downstairs, washed my face, changed my top into something less casual, and put on lipstick. All of a sudden, a festive mood washed over me, and I decided to add eye shadow, mascara, and blush. I pulled back my long curly hair and put on green dangly earrings matching my eyes. I looked good. I even saw a hint of sparkle around me. I studied my reflection and could see how my pool of self-trust was filling again. I felt more like myself than I had in a very long time. Puzzling had re-centered me easily and painlessly. Yikes! I was becoming a mini-Grace. I could do far worse.

I went downstairs and found the family gathered in the living room in front of an inevitable fire. Everyone remarked on how pretty I looked and it made me happy they noticed. It was a cozy scene with Gus stretched out in front of the fire. Also inevitable.

Special hors d'oeuvres held pride-of-place on the coffee table and I recognized my father's handiwork. A bottle of champagne chilled in an ice bucket. "What's the occasion?" I asked. "Are we getting an early start to Aunt Grace's party?"

Dad stood to open the champagne as Grace responded, "No, we're completing step *ten* together with your parents. Once you have honored what you accomplished, it's time to celebrate. This is what we're going to do now. Before we begin, though, we must first disassemble the puzzle. Like completing a chapter of a book, you don't want to begin another until you've turned the page on the old. Why don't we first take care of step *ten* before officially celebrating?"

Grace and I walked into the sunroom and once again stood for a few minutes to admire the puzzle. I was moved to thank the puzzle out loud for what it had taught me and to thank Grace as well for her guidance and suggestions throughout this process. Then, with what I can only call reverence, we broke the puzzle apart and put it back in the box.

We ceremoniously carried the puzzle to the living room and positioned it in the center of the fireplace mantle. I returned to the sunroom to unfold the craft table and lean it against a wall. I would return it later to the basement if Dad didn't beat me to it. I carried the two chairs we used to their original places in the living room, and then made sure the fire was out; closed the flue; and turned off the lights. Our puzzling was well and truly over.

A sweet melancholy filled me. This was an extraordinary journey taken with a deceptively simple tool with a particularly sagacious aunt. *The Zen of Puzzles*. I listened and learned. I had changed.

I walked into the living room and picked up my glass of champagne. We each offered a toast to the puzzle, to ourselves, and to our futures. I thanked Grace for leading me through the ten-step process of puzzling, the ten-step process of living life. "Ah," Grace said, "but there's yet one more step. It's not enough to have experiences, to learn new things about yourself, and then simply tuck them away. Step *eleven*, Rachel, is living your life with more gusto and greater love as a result of everything you've learned. Step *eleven* is the capstone of all your puzzle experiences.

"*The Zen of Puzzles* is not just about listening and learning, but about *becoming different* as a result. It's about becoming enlightened as you fill yourself with light, shine it into the world, and lessen the darkness of crippling fear.

"Truly, you've been given the time and resources to become clear about how your life can really work. This is a gift beyond measure, and simply by being a beacon on a hill, shining your light and radiating your love, you will bring hope. You will inspire others.

"Strive for Divine Selfishness with the highest integrity and all else will follow. I promise you. Have fun with this, Rachel, and seek the adventure of it all."

We looked at each other, feeling pretty emotional. We were truly blessed and we knew it. In the warm glow of fire, family, and dog, we finished the bottle of champagne and opened another. We celebrated the completion of the process. All was truly well.

Epilogue

felt quite beautiful the night of the party. I, too, had purchased a special dress for the occasion and the shimmering, soft-gold color did all the right things to lighten and brighten, soften and enhance. Everyone seemed to glitter just a little more brilliantly than usual and my mother's dress was a big hit. It certainly captured my father's undivided attention. His amazed and very appreciative look made us all laugh.

Mom had done a wonderful job making the arrangements for the party, even ordering a stunning sunset in a sky radiantly rich after the storm. The forces of nature had fully cooperated. Love is in the details.

Those from out-of-town all arrived and enthusiastically entered into the spirit of the evening. Unfortunately, my friend, Fiona, who really wanted to come with her husband, had called to say they were both on sick-children duty. She heard all about it from me later, though!

The dinner was delicious and the toasts to Grace, heartfelt and moving—a wonderful tribute to a woman who inspired so many for so long.

Grace was a good sport about the roast my father organized after dinner. Several of her friends were wickedly funny and like seasoned entertainers, they knew how to play to their audience. My father almost stole the show with his *Grace after Meals* monologue, relating choice bits of after-dinner conversations with Grace throughout the years. I had not heard the more adult parts before, and I laughed as hard as everyone else as I listened to the stories for the first time.

After the roast, Grace thanked everyone for coming and offered special thanks to my parents for arranging the event. She talked for only a few minutes about her life, but she did this in her usual gracious and humorous way. By the end of this after-dinner segue, the mood was pretty mellow and warm affection flowed freely.

Grace and Antonio surprised everyone by starting the dancing with a beautiful tango they had secretly practiced. Ninety years old and still with a dancer's limber moves. Even then, she was able to weave mystery, beauty, and power into her every gesture, and Antonio was her perfect foil. We watched as they shimmered and sizzled across the floor, and Aunt Grace's unabashed pleasure and delight were evident. This is what she meant by step *eleven*—the living of life—passionately, whole-heartedly, in full measure. Grace was full of grace, well-named and well-loved.

Revelry

Everyone danced the entire night and no one was allowed to just sit and watch for too long. Robert and Gina never stopped for a minute and, at one point around midnight, they got everyone into a conga line when the energy began to wane. Even the wait staff joined in as I guessed they were getting tired as well. After the conga, the party caught its second wind and the dancing, singing, and story-telling continued nonstop.

With lots of mixing-and-mingling, I met truly fascinating people from twenty-somethings to ninety-somethings. Each time I looked around, I noticed that every person genuinely seemed to be having a happy time. A special feeling enveloped those assembled, and no one wanted to have this rarified event end. Grace's ninetieth birthday party was universally declared an enormous success, truly a cherished time to be remembered.

At 2:00 AM the lights came back to full brightness, a signal the gathering was formally, though reluctantly, over. Another hour passed before all the final goodbyes were said and partiers left for various hotels and B&Bs. I later heard the celebrating spilled into impromptu get-togethers throughout the day on Sunday as travelers, apparently unwilling to return home, kept finding excuses to delay their departures.

Of course, we were the last to leave at 3:00 AM. I could not believe Grace and Antonio were still going strong, pumped by excitement and fun. We ended up inviting a few of Grace's closest friends to return home with us where we proceeded to relive each minute of Grace's party. We mainlined coffee, swapped stories, laughed, and even cried a little. These un-orchestrated moments were tender and unrepeatable. Finally, however, we all wound down and by 4:30 AM, even Grace was ready to call it a night.

By late Sunday afternoon, everyone had gone home except me. When I wandered downstairs at noon, my tired but elated mother told me Robert and Gina said good-bye. They had left earlier to pick up their children and intended to call me the next day. Hours later, like everyone else, I kept finding excuses not to leave. Gus even got his long-awaited beach run.

Since Grace and Antonio were staying, I really wanted to hang around a few more days, but I needed to get back to work. It was time to go. When I said good-bye to Grace, I held her in a long hug, not wanting to release this special woman and this magical time.

Grace gently pulled me away, held me at arm's length, and smiled lovingly. With her characteristic twinkle she said, "There's a secret formula for life I'm now going to bestow from one Master Puzzler to another. This will complete your full initiation into the proud and ancient order of Puzzlers. Are you ready? Here's the secret formula.

"Wholly engage each life experience that comes to you. Let it go with gratitude when it's time. Cherish and hold dear the memories you have created.

"You've come to the end of an important chapter, dear one. Let it go and turn the page. Remember it fondly and with gratitude. Then put your attention on what's happening in the present and envision what's coming next. Only then can you live the change you've become."

My heart was too full to say anything profound or intelligent. I nodded, smiled back, hugged her quickly one more time, and then left. After a short drive, I sat silently in the car with Dad until the ferry came, and gave him a hard hug when I got out. He understood.

Epilogue

Reverie

On the passage to New York, I again felt the familiar sweet melancholy often sneaking in when a beautiful time comes to an end. Then, like a digitalized slide show, the memories of the week—Aunt Grace, the puzzling, the family, Gus, the stories, the storm, the party, Antonio, the tango—flashed on my mental screen, and I embraced and relished every single one. It was quite a week. What wonderful memories we had made!

After Party

My life was different after the puzzle experience. I would like to say I miraculously and immediately transformed, but this would be grossly dishonest. However, I was happy to report to Aunt Grace things did shift a little more each day as I practiced what I had learned.

I punctuated work with more walks. I enjoyed extending myself to a greater number of people. I took more risks—small ones at first and then greater ones. I was happier and more relaxed. I became a better daughter, aunt, niece, friend, lover, boss, and team member. Each small course correction brought me to new places I could never before have imagined. Yes, it took time, but I was on my way.

Grace and Antonio came to my wedding three years after her big party. They repeated (though a little more slowly) the fabled tango from her ninetieth birthday much to the delight of those who missed it the first time.

Richard, my new husband, had heard all about the party and asked them to perform the dance at our reception as a special surprise for me. What a guy! He wanted this special memory to become part of our own celebration.

Since Grace and Antonio considered Richard to be "one of their own" and responded to him as they would to me, they immediately and enthusiastically said *yes* to his request. They again brought down the house.

Grace was also with us to celebrate the birth of our first child, Kate—Katherine Grace McKeating. Grace said she was delighted to be a great-great aunt again, but I could see how the years were beginning to weigh on her. She was now ninety-five. Shortly after the family gathering for Kate's christening, Grace died peacefully in her sleep. Antonio called us the next day, and though expected, the news left everyone shaken and sad. A part of me had hoped she would live forever.

Going Home

Grace left instructions for the *eleventh* step—the capstone of her life's long process—and there was a grand honoring of this remarkable woman. No—let me be more precise—there was a blowout party at New York's Ritz Carlton to celebrate Grace's life—just as she had planned it.

Six months before she died, Grace had paid for the party in full and carefully selected the guests, invitations, band, flowers, dinnerware, glassware, serving pieces, table-cloths, napkins, candles, food, and drinks for the event.

As she frequently said, love is in the details. Her attorney was given clear directions about guest invitations, vendor receipts, and after-party tips. He knew exactly what to do.

Grace even got the date right, and the event was held three weeks after she died, executed according to her meticulous directives. I was not a bit surprised.

As a final gesture, Grace had recorded a message to be played after the dinner, leaving no dry eyes among those gathered. So many of her touches filled the party space I half-expected her to walk through the door at any second.

Nicely done, Aunt Grace. Nicely done.

When Antonio later went to her safe deposit box, he found letters addressed to him, to each of her family members, and to her closest friends—her way of saying final good-byes to those she loved most. I treasure her letter and the aquamarine and diamond ring she enclosed which Uncle George gave her on the twenty-fifth anniversary of their partnership, a gift he said would match her eyes. With Antonio's blessing, she also generously gave me the deed to her Manhattan home.

Richard became very emotional when he read Grace's long letter to him and walked for hours trying to absorb everything she had written. Like me, he continues to draw upon her strength. We are enormously grateful for the opportunity to raise our children in a home holding so much of Grace's spirit, in a place integral to my own growing-up years.

People marveled at Grace's sensing the time of her death since she did not die of any particular illness. Her great heart simply stopped beating, probably just like she had planned it. However, Grace had told Antonio she knew the time for her to leave was coming and she wanted him to be prepared. Grace said she would die within six months. She beat her deadline by five days.

After Grace died, Antonio sold his business and condo and moved back to Italy. He wanted to spend his last years with his family though he returns regularly to New York and, at our insistence, stays with us. We visited him in Italy once but at this point in our lives, it is hard to travel with two small energetic children but it is always a cheerful reunion when we do manage to get together.

My parents have seen Antonio in Italy more frequently. He continues to do well and seems to be happier though he misses Grace terribly, as we all do. *Grace Stories* always come up in conversation whenever we meet, softening the pain by remembering the good times. The edges of sharp sadness have rounded to fond remembrance.

Sometimes I sit by Kate's bed and watch her sleeping, hoping one day I can pass Grace's legacy of love, joy, and wisdom to her. In those quiet moments, I feel a whisper of Grace's presence and the slightest touch on my cheek. I can almost hear her voice reminding me, "Keep the sacred pact with yourself and the Divine presence within you, and all good things will naturally follow. I promise you this. All is well, darling Rachel. All is well."

The Zen of Puzzles Process

A Ritual for Accessing the Subconscious Mind

BEFORE WORKING THE PUZZLE

1. Let go of any strong emotions distressing you about a situation or person you want to release in order to create the *inner space* for new information.

2. Once you have cleared constricting emotions, begin to dream bigger dreams and reach for more expansive positive feelings. Fill yourself with possibilities no matter how illogical they might seem.

3. Declare what you want to experience in the next chapter of your life.

THE PUZZLE STEPS

Step One

Select a puzzle which pleases you and will help achieve your puzzle intention.

Step Two

Set your boundaries and the expectations of those around you by letting them know who is permitted to work your puzzle.

Step Three

Be sure your table or work surface is large enough to accommodate the puzzle size (and your dreams!) and leaves room for your work/play.

Step Four

Create a partnership with your subconscious mind by stating your puzzle intention aloud and asking the subconscious to put together and deliver the information you need either as you work the puzzle or sleep. Thank this part of your mind in advance for its help.

Step Five

The night before you work the puzzle, ready yourself for assembly by sorting the puzzle pieces by color and design; putting the border together (if applicable); and moving the grouped pieces to the border section closest to its color. If you wish, you can also sort the pieces by shape.

Step Six

After "sleeping on it" and observing the puzzle pieces in a clearer light, sort each pile more finely by color and design.

Step Seven

Begin working the puzzle by choosing pieces with colors that please you most. When you work, honor each piece and notice the emerging patterns as you join it to others. Feel how satisfying it is to connect each section. Check in with yourself and remain aware of what you are learning. Journaling or recording your insights is always a good idea during this step. Don't become a "puzzle martyr" by sitting too long and taxing your body.

Step Eight

Complete the puzzle. Then admire the puzzle and honor your work.

Step Nine

Take the time to think about what you have discovered about yourself and how your original puzzle intention was met. Let the experience be real to you. Let it sink in.

Step Ten

Thank the puzzle for what it taught you before dissembling it. Then celebrate your accomplishment. (As Grace would say, champagne and chocolate are great when you reach this step, but do what pleases you most. Create a "chocolate moment" of the heart.)

Step Eleven

Take what you have learned from puzzling and whole heartedly incorporate the new insights into your life. Remember to shine your light!

A Few Questions You Might Consider

The question sets below pertain to the key subjects of each chapter. They can be helpful in guiding you when you make your own inner journey. As you work with the questions either by yourself or with trusted friends, you can pretend you're discussing them with Aunt Grace and see what she has to say!

PROLOGUE

People Who Positively Impacted Your Life

Looking back, who positively impacted your life? What is your favorite memory of them? What did you learn? How do you continue to honor them and what they taught you?

Handling a Difficult Time

Who had a negative impact on your life? How did your life change as a result of this experience? Who helped you through it? If you are still carrying the effects of this difficult situation, what will you do now to minimize its impact?

Experiencing Death

When was it hard for you to get over the death of someone you loved? What form did your grief take? How did you release the experience while still keeping the person in your heart? If you haven't been able to do so yet, what actions will you now take?

CHAPTER ONE: MEET AUNT GRACE

Being Controlled

When have you felt like you were forced to do things you didn't want to do? How did you handle this? What were your feelings during the controlling time and when it was finally over? (If it's not over, how would you *like to feel* in the future, and how can you get there?) How might being controlled by someone make you feel justified in controlling others (if applicable)? How can this approach harm you over time?

Self-Talk during Difficult Times

If you've been in a difficult situation, what was the *inner story* you told yourself to get you through? What actions did you take to change your environment, and where did you get the courage to take this step? Did you change, did the other person change, or did you both change? How? What did you learn? If you're still in a bad situation, what are you going to do about it now?

Judgements

Everyone has done something they regret which others might judge as bad or wrong behavior. When have you judged others about what they did in the past? When have others judged you? When have you judged yourself? What steps might you take to more quickly notice when you are judging yourself or others? How can you learn to see others as they are in the present and not how they were in the past?

CHAPTER TWO:
THE PURPOSE OF PUZZLING

When Relationships End

When a relationship ends and you get hurt, do you usually blame the other person? What responsibility do you take for the part you played in its ending? Did you talk to the person about what happened and how it impacted you? Why or why not? If this were an intimate relationship, how did you ensure you parted and remained friends or, if you have children, come to an agreement about custody and co-parenting? How did you help your children grieve for their loss? How did you mourn the relationship so you could let it go without holding onto potentially poisonous emotions?

Great Clothes

How do your clothes typically make you feel? How would you *like* to feel in your clothes *in your current body size*? What kind of clothes can you purchase to help get you to this good-feeling space? If you don't have good-feeling clothes in your closet, why not? If your budget is tight, have you explored thrift stores or online clothing rental sites for deals on great clothes? Why not?

The Relationship Rulebook

Consciously or subconsciously, how were you taught relationships should work? Have you been obeying the unwritten rules in a *relationship rulebook* you may have unconsciously inherited as a child? Does the relationship rulebook still make sense? How have you modified it to make it your own? If you've never thought about this, what will be your next step now?

CHAPTER THREE: MYSTERIES OF THE MIND

Developing Subconscious Programs

How did you learn the *right-and-proper* way to think, feel, and act? Are you still driven by the subconscious programs you inherited fashioning your attitudes, beliefs, and values? How do you know if you are or are not still driven by them? How can you become more aware of your biases to better manage them? Do you really want to change your conscious behaviors and your subconscious knee-jerk reactions? Why or why not? Who can help you change without judging you?

Emotions

Emotions are meant to give you immediate feedback about what is going on inside. How do you keep in touch with your emotions? Which emotions do you label positive or negative, and why? How can both types of emotions help you grow and change? When do you normally hang onto your negative emotions? What is the "mental story" you tell yourself to justify giving these emotions too much of your attention? How does fixating on negative emotions affect you? What can you do to notice them and release them more quickly?

Making Things Happen

What dreams have you had for years which have not yet manifested? Why is this? Are these dreams still possible for you? Why or why not? What limitations do you impose upon yourself that keep your dreams from coming true? What dreams have you postponed because you don't know how to take action on them? Who can help you with this? What dreams from childhood or adolescence are no longer appropriate for you as an adult and should be discarded? As you grow and change, how do you ensure your dreams grow truer and clearer as you do? Do you take the time to dream? How can you build more dreaming into your life? (Hint: daydreams are just as important as night dreams.)

CHAPTER FOUR: THE BEGINNING

Accessing Internal Information

When do you pay attention to your inner voices, both the voice always criticizing you and the one quietly delivering helpful messages? Which one do you normally listen to? How can you learn to listen more closely to the voice speaking your greatest truth? Where does your criticizing voice come from? How can you practice ignoring it? What funny things can you say to this judgmental voice to lighten you up and make it go away?

Using Rituals

What rituals did you inherit? Where did they come from? Do they continue to serve you well? If not, why do you still keep doing them? What rituals have you consciously or subconsciously developed to make your routine tasks easier? How can you use rituals to gather information from the subconscious mind? What steps will you take to practice accessing your subconscious mind more easily?

Being Supported

Who are the people in your life you can really talk to from the heart? When are you reluctant to tell them the truth? Why do you think you do this? Is it easier for you to support others or be supported by them? Why is that? What can you do to create a better balance?

CHAPTER FIVE: PUTTING IT ALL TOGETHER

Changing Your Mind

Once you make a decision, do you examine it later after time has passed and given you greater perspective? Why or why not? What quick decision have you made you wish you had paid more attention to? When you became aware of your too-quick decision, what did you do with your new understanding? Do you believe once you make up your mind about something, you should not change that decision no matter what? Where does this belief come from? When has this belief served you and when has it gotten in the way?

Duty and Obligation

How do the *shoulds* of your life get in the way of taking care of yourself? When do you feel guilty when you love yourself first, and where does this feeling of guilt come from? When you're being honest with yourself, how many of your actions are prompted by love and how many by duty and obligation? How can you begin to act more from love? What would loving yourself first look like to you?

Sharing the Load

When do you take on more than you should? Where does this sense of false responsibility come from? When are you too nice at the expense of your own happiness? What can you do about this knee-jerk reaction? Who might be willing to take on the responsibilities you want to let go? What has stopped you from doing that? What would your life look like if you had the courage to *do what you want with harm to none?* Do you even want to live this way? Why or why not? What's stopping you and what can you do about it?

CHAPTER SIX: KEEPING FAITH

Transitions

What triggered the major transitions of your life? How did you work through them? Who helped you? What did you learn? Did you handle them right away? Why or why not? Did you have a role model who taught you how to move through transitions? What did they teach you? How can you become more courageous in making future transitions?

Negotiating

With your primary relationships, how do you negotiate what you want and need? How willing are you to speak your truth and make your needs known? How can you become better at negotiating and advocating for what you need and want, especially when it feels risky to speak up? How much freedom do you allow in a relationship both for yourself and the other person?

Pleasing Yourself

Do you know what pleases you and makes you happy? How do you ensure that others know and respect the choices you make? What tasks do you find annoying or boring? How can you give them a different meaning so you can perform them with love? How can you connect your daily routine to a bigger life picture? How can you make your routines sacred?

CHAPTER SEVEN: THE GNARLY SIDE OF PUZZLING

Living Your Own Life

How have you unconsciously adopted aspects of another person's life and made them your own? Do these aspects serve you? If not, how can you let them go? What would your most authentic life look like? What steps can you take to initiate a truer life? Who might get upset by this and why? Would you allow them to stop you? How can you get the support you need to change?

Being in the Flow

What happens in your life when you're out of the flow? How do you know when you're in the flow? How can you learn to more easily enter the flow and re-center? How can those close to you help you learn to relax and take care of yourself? Do you always allow them to help? Why or why not?

Warrior and Adventurer Aspects

Do you consider yourself to embody more of the qualities of a warrior or an adventurer? When do you function in each? When do you struggle or fight when you don't need to? How do your behaviors change under stress? How do you practice strengthening the personal qualities you want to develop? What small steps can you take to change the way you routinely approach situations in order to make your life easier?

CHAPTER EIGHT: FINDING A WAY

Turning Points

What was a pivotal time when you made a decision eventually sending your life in a different direction?

What did you learn? Conversely, when did you decide *not* to go in a truer direction because fear or discomfort held you back? What was the consequence of making a default decision to not move forward? How would you handle the situation differently today?

Being a Victim

In what situations do you feel powerless—incapable of changing a situation? Is this actually the truth or part of the mental story you tell yourself? What can you do to take back your power from the situation? If it doesn't make sense to change a situation immediately, what steps can you take now which will lead to a resolution in the future? Who can support you in this process? When have you stayed too long in a bad situation? What benefits did staying stuck offer you—what did you get out of it? How can you find the courage to change?

Relationships

When you meet new people, how do you know if you would like to get to know them better? When have you been wrong about moving ahead and later discovered the person was not what you expected? How have these experiences helped sharpen your instincts when deciding to pursue potential relationships? How can you become more open to meeting different kinds of people rather than immediately sorting them into predetermined categories? Where do these categories come from and how do they reflect the values you hold today? How can you change your relationship with inanimate objects and learn to value them more? How does respecting inanimate objects allow them to better serve you?

CHAPTER NINE:
THE TOOLS OF ATTENTION

Self-Consciousness

What distractions take your focus away from what you're doing and how do they make you feel self-conscious? When are you more focused on your performance than on the people around you? How might not noticing or focusing on others make you appear to them? How can you change? Do you want to? Why or why not?

Expectations

How have negative or low expectations of your abilities or talents impacted the outcome of a task you worked on? How do your high or low expectations of others influence the way you see them? Whose standards or values shape your high or low expectations? Where do these standards come from? How can you learn to manage your negative expectations of others and see them more honestly? What is the best way to help others view you more accurately?

The Warm Pebble

How can you apply the story of the warm pebble to your life? What personal enlightenment are you seeking? How does this search help you? What form does your search take? Who guides or shares your search? How can you use their teaching to help others? When will it be time for you to transition from being a full-time student of life to becoming a teacher? How will you know you have arrived at this point? When have you thrown something important away out of habit or inattention? What did you do about the situation? How can you remain more conscious in the future?

CHAPTER TEN:
THE MIDDLE AND THE END

Mid-Process Blahs

When you're working on a project, when do you tend to get tired of what you're doing? How do you know when to take a break or slow things down? When have you pushed through a low-energy period and known later you made a mistake? What did you learn? Who (or what inner voice) commands you to "keep going no matter what" when doing so will deplete you? What can you do to change this situation?

Mistakes

How do you feel when you change your mind about a person or event, or realize you've made a mistake and need to correct it? Your reaction is a learned behavior, so who taught you to think about your mistakes this way? Looking back, what did you learn when you changed your mind or corrected a mistake? If you judge yourself after you making a mistake, how can you be kinder to yourself? When do you judge others for the mistakes they make? How can you look at their mistakes simply as opportunities to grow and change? (There's a hint here for judging your own mistakes.)

Endings

How do you feel when you've come to an end of a project, process, or relationship you have enjoyed and valued? Do you take the time to honor them, thank them, and celebrate how you handled the transition? Why or why not? What will you do differently about endings in the future? What small and big events can you celebrate for yourself and those you love?

EPILOGUE

Legacy

Who shared their legacy with you? What was their legacy and how are you applying what they gave you? How can you demonstrate this legacy more fully in your day-to-day life and with others? What is your own personal legacy? Who will you want to pass it to? How do you intend to do that? When will you get started?

Holding On

When do you tend to hold onto people and situations when it's time to let them go? Why do you think you do that? How can you learn to let go more easily? Who can help you with this? How can you call on your warrior and adventurer aspects to help? When have you used these personality aspects to make your life better? When have you misused them? What do they each teach you about yourself?

Changing

When and why do you postpone changes you need to make? How will you know when you have been successful at making the changes you want? How do you make changes? Who helps or hinders you? What can you do about those who want to hold you back? At the end of each year, how do you measure whether it was a good or not-so-good year? At the end of your life, what will you tell yourself about how you have lived, what you have learned, and how well you have loved?

Acknowledgements

Though you certainly know who you are, you might not fully realize the incredible difference your support and wisdom made throughout this writing process—from book concept to publication and the celebrations beyond. Therefore, please humor me one more time and listen with your heart to these words.

I honor those who encouraged and exhorted, especially Rae who helped me understand it was time and supported me chapter-by-chapter; who did her lawyerly thing throughout; and who cheered me on every step of the way. I am very grateful to Sharon who read the initial draft and whose work and insights kept me centered during the writing process. Many sincere thanks go to Anne who made great suggestions and such intelligent, important edits with her usual tact and kindness. A gigantic thank you as well to my brother, John Michael, who always believed.

Heartfelt thanks to my additional readers—Bill, Dave M., Marcia, Nicholas, Shannon, and Shawn. I acknowledge those who were willing to read the book but life got in the way. Next time!

Finally, enthusiastic kudos to the special and gifted team at Luminare Press. Thanks to Patricia, a fellow

Acknowledgements

Master Puzzler, and Luminare's remarkable owner, editor, and publisher who made the publishing process easy and fun for this first-time author. To the amazingly talented graphic designer, Claire, who truly listened and got the cover just right. Finally, to Kim, expert project manager and remarkably patient copy editor, who made sure the book would be proud of itself and helped me become a better writer. I look forward to working with you all again on the next Zen book!

Printed in the USA
CPSIA information can be obtained
at www.ICGtesting.com
LVHW021237090923
757633LV00019B/19/J

9 781944 733364